The
WHODUNNIT
Puzzle
Book

Dr Gareth Moore B.Sc (Hons) M.Phil Ph.D is the internationally best-selling author of a wide range of brain-training and puzzle books for both children and adults, including *Enigma: Crack the Code, Ultimate Dot to Dot, Brain Games for Clever Kids, Lateral Logic* and *Extreme Mazes*. His books have sold millions of copies in the UK alone, and have been published in over thirty different languages. He is also the creator of online brain-training site BrainedUp.com, and runs the daily puzzle site PuzzleMix.com.

Web:	DrGarethMoore.com
Twitter:	@DrGarethMoore
YouTube:	YouTube.com/@DrGareth

Laura Jayne Ayres is a puzzle writer and researcher. After studying Linguistics at the University of Cambridge, she worked as a playwright before joining Dr Gareth Moore's puzzle team. Books that she has worked on include *Hacked: The Cyber Crime Puzzle Book, The Great British Puzzle Book, The Perfect Crime Puzzle Book, The Nautical Puzzle Book* and *The Ordnance Survey Kids' Adventure Book*.

The WHODUNNIT Puzzle Book

Dr Gareth Moore
& Laura Jayne Ayres

Michael O'Mara Books Limited

First published in Great Britain in 2023 by
Michael O'Mara Books Limited
9 Lion Yard
Tremadoc Road
London SW4 7NQ

A CIP catalogue record for this book is available from the British Library.

Papers used by Michael O'Mara Books Limited are natural, recyclable
products made from wood grown in sustainable forests. The manufacturing
processes conform to the environmental regulations of the country of
origin.

ISBN: 978-1-78929-582-5 in paperback print format

2 3 4 5 6 7 8 9 10

Designed and typeset by Any Puzzle Media Ltd
Includes images from Adobe Stock and from Shutterstock.com
Cover design by Natasha Le Coultre
Cover assets from Shutterstock.com

Printed and bound by CPI Group (UK) Ltd, Croydon, CR0 4YY

www.mombooks.com

Contents

Introduction 6

The Cases

Ticket to Die 9

A Bump in the Road 33

The Forced Hand 47

A Whole New Ball Game...........................61

Painted into a Corner...............................75

The Writing on the Wall 91

A Dramatic Ending 113

Cold Comfort 127

The Diamond and the Rough 141

The Plot Thickens 155

Detective Skills......................................179

Solutions 191

Introduction

Welcome to *The Whodunnit Puzzle Book*, in which you can help solve ten cosy-crime scenarios from the comfort of your own home.

On the following pages are the notes of Mrs Whitstable, renowned amateur detective and resident of the village of Bishop's End. She will take you through ten of her most intriguing cases in such a way that you can crack them along with her, unravelling mysteries as you solve the puzzles on each page. There are murders, thefts and forgeries to get to the bottom of, and plenty of shady characters to meet along the way.

Full solutions – and explanations, where necessary – are included at the back of the book, referenced by page number.

Without further ado, it's time to introduce you to Mrs Whitstable. We hope you have as much fun working your way through the book as we did in making it.

Happy solving!

Dr Gareth Moore   Laura Jayne Ayres

Hello dear reader,

I understand you may be interested in
some of my most famous cases, and
I can hardly blame you. I moved to
Bishop's End several decades ago on
the assumption that it would be a quiet
place to live, and I have never been more
delighted to be so wrong about something.
There is a disproportionate amount of
disquiet and deception in this quaint little village, and my detective
skills have been frequently put to work during my time here.

Several of my most well-known cases – as well as a couple of my
lesser-known mysteries – have been gathered together in this
book for you to work your way through, each labelled with the
name by which it became best known in the newspapers at the
time. Facsimilies of evidence I collected at the time are displayed
liberally throughout, always accompanied with my notes and hints
that you'll need to solve that particular puzzle. You'll note that I
always include a little 'to do' note to myself, to remind me how to
get started on each conundrum. There's also a prompt question at
the bottom-right of each pair of facing puzzle pages, so once you've
answered this you'll know you're done with that puzzle.

I recommend working through the book in the order in which it is
presented, from front to back. There are a few characters and places
which pop up more than once, and snippets of information that may
come in handy in a later case too. Personally, I usually like to work
alone when I'm solving a crime (or a crossword puzzle) but you are
welcome to tackle them with as many friends or acquaintances as
you care to gather.

Once you have got to the bottom of all ten crimes, there is an
additional 'detective skills' segment for the most beady-eyed among
you, where you can test your observation and memory. Let's just say
you'll do well to pay attention to each and every detail I've included
in the cases, no matter how insignificant it may seem at first!

Good luck,

Mrs Whitstable

TICKET TO DIE

Another Case Solved by

Mrs Agnes Whitstable

Ticket to Die

Every now and again, I am called away from Bishop's End on business of one sort or another. I find city life rather dull and predictable, so I do try to avoid travelling into the urban world as much as possible. After all, life in Bishop's End provides plenty of entertainment as it is – not to mention the occasional murder.

Sometimes, however, travel is unavoidable. Several years ago, I was journeying home from a trip to the local city of Flintchester. The exact details escape me now but I believe I had been in pursuit of a new cheese grater and simply could not get my hands on one in the village. I had travelled by train in search of my culinary quarry and was returning in the evening – and it was a beautiful summer's evening, too, filled with birdsong. Unfortunately, for one man, it was also filled with bloodshed.

A murder had been committed at Flintchester rail station mere hours earlier, on the very platform at which I was supposed to board the train back to my beloved Bishop's End. Indeed, it was the very same platform I had alighted onto earlier that day. Imagine my surprise! Another murder in my midst. It seems that I can't go anywhere without someone shuffling off their mortal coil.

The victim was a Mr Norris, a geography teacher at a school not far from Bishop's End who, if I remember, taught Mr Weston's two boys. Mr Weston runs the bakery in Bishop's End, and a fine job of it he does too.

Just the right amount of texture in the crust. But I digress; his sons' one-time geography teacher had just met an untimely end at the hands of an unknown killer who – much to the horror of several journey-goers – had fled the scene on a train.

Perhaps most intriguing of all was the discovery of several postcards around the body of poor Mr Norris. The postcards had been sent to his home address from all over the world and, seemingly, from the killer. Who was this well-travelled murderer who was so keen to keep in touch with his hapless victim?

The policeman on duty at the station was a fellow I didn't recognize, but who introduced himself as Graham – which might have been either his first or second name. Given that he was clearly not a man for detail, I set about trying to find this mysterious killer myself.

So here are my case notes on the matter. There are eight bits of evidence to ponder over, and the small matter of a murder to solve. So what are you waiting for? It's time to track down a cold-blooded killer.

To solve the mystery, you'll need to establish answers to the following questions:

1. **Where** had the killer travelled most recently?

2. **What** was the murder weapon?

3. **Where** did the attack take place?

4. **Where** did the murderer flee to?

5. **What** was the murderer's name?

And, as always, keep an eye out for any other suspicious happenings while you solve. You never know what might come in handy later!

Good luck,

Mrs Whitstable

Ticket to Die

Death by a Thousand Stamps

I personally love to receive post, but I suppose in this case you could call it harassment. These sinister postcards were sent in the months preceding poor Mr Norris' murder. Whoever the killer is, they're clearly well-travelled.

To do: work out the order in which the countries were visited by the killer. The final location is the place they travelled from to commit the murder

Bonjour from the Eiffel Tower! Your demise soon, but Canada next.

A day on the Nile, very inspiring. China tomorrow and, later, your death.

Greetings from Niagara Falls, as your downfall approaches. But first, South Africa.

Saying sayonara to Japan today, then off to Berlin, then off with your head!

Lovely day in Machu Picchu! Next stop, Egypt. And soon, murder!

Table Mountain today. Death is imminent, but Mount Fuji is more so.

Walked along the Great Wall today, just as you sleepwalk to your demise. Paris next!

Where was the murderer coming from?

_____

Ticket to Die

Some Strings Attached

Instead of strolling into the station already armed, our murderer rummaged through the lost property office to find their weapon of choice.

Each of the lost suitcases had a label with details of the contents within, in case the old owner came a-looking. The labels, however, had since become damaged, and the letters in the words of each item were now jumbled up.

According to Graham, the weapon was taken from the suitcase whose contents otherwise had the most clothing.

BAG 1

CKSOS

WCHAT

ANOKRA

UNOJARL

PEEPWARNS

INKEF

To do: unscramble the suitcase labels and work out which one the murder weapon was taken from

BAG 2

OWE BIT

CAVEROOT

GAINCARD

RORRIM

OWLET

I SNOOP

BAG 3

EDSSR

VETS

MAINGAZE

HOSES

BLUETL

LETLAW

BAG 4

SORERUST

TRISH

FARSC

VOGELS

ITUS

OZARR

What was the murder weapon?

_____

15

Ticket to Die
Rather Negative, Actually

Poor Mr Norris seems to have been something of a trainspotter; perhaps that's how our killer knew where to track him down. He was certainly a photographer, in any case. It appeared our victim took a few pictures of the platform on which he was attacked before stumbling into the waiting room where his body was found.

The negatives became damaged after the camera hit the ground, but it's possible to piece together some of the images of the platform.

To do: use the part-developed photos to reveal the platform number on which Mr Norris was attacked

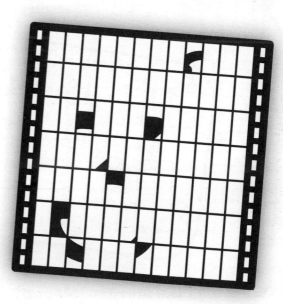

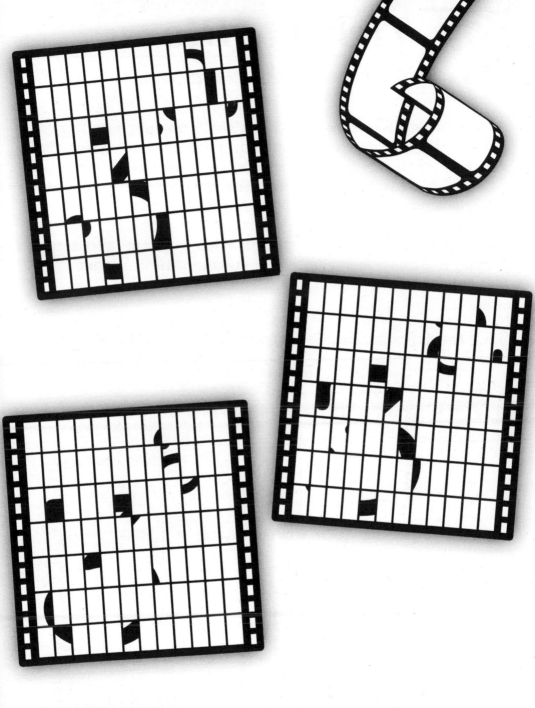

On which platform was Mr Norris attacked?

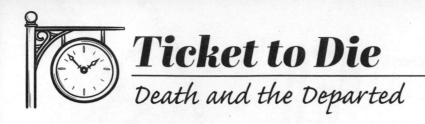

Ticket to Die
Death and the Departed

I seem to always be delayed when I travel by rail, but apparently our murderer had no problem making a swift getaway. With the body not discovered until later, and no witnesses actually having seen the murderer escape, the killer's movements had to be deduced by logic.

After some terse conversation with Graham, and some more pleasant chatter with the station guard, it was possible to put together this timetable – of sorts.

Notes from a most pleasant discussion with station guard Mr Richard Trackson:

- Between 16.30 and 17.30, only five platforms had train departures, of which each only had one: 2, 3a, 4, 6 and 7b

- The St Church train left at 17.10

- The Stickleton train left two minutes before the Drumberry train

- The train at platform 2 left nine minutes before the train at platform 7b

- The train at platform 3a departed for Drumberry

- The train at platform 4 departed at 16.30

- The train to Little Bizenforth left at 16.48

- The train to Lopton Head left at 17.01

- None of the trains had the same departure time

Notes from a somewhat bristly conversation with Graham, police officer on duty:

- The murder was committed sometime after 16.40

- The murderer had fled by 17.00

- The murderer did not depart from platform 7b, whose train was the last to leave in the hour window

To do: *deduce the murderer's getaway details*

From which platform did the murderer leave?

_____

What was the time of departure?

_____

What was their destination?

_____

Ticket to Die

Covering One's Tracks

Apparently having not yet sufficiently embarrassed the local police force, our slippery killer attempted a further act of misdirection before leaving Flintchester. The tracks at the station were once controlled by two turntables which altered the directions of departing trains. According to the guard, the murderer sneaked into the control room and gave the old track-turners a quick spin.

I made a rough sketch – shown on the opposite page – showing how the tracks usually line up, with the two circles each representing a turntable. According to the station guard, **both** turntables were rotated 180 degrees before the killer's train left the station, thus altering the planned destination of the train.

The platform on which the murderer boarded the train had already been established, though do turn back a page if you haven't deduced that yet (or if, indeed, your memory fails you – it does happen).

To do: mentally rotate the turntables 180 degrees each to reveal the killer's new lettered destination

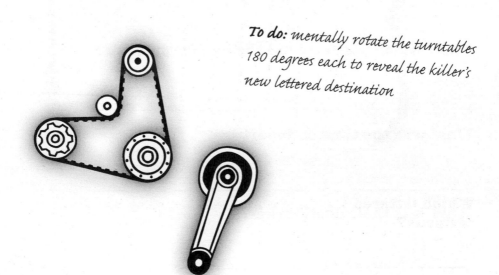

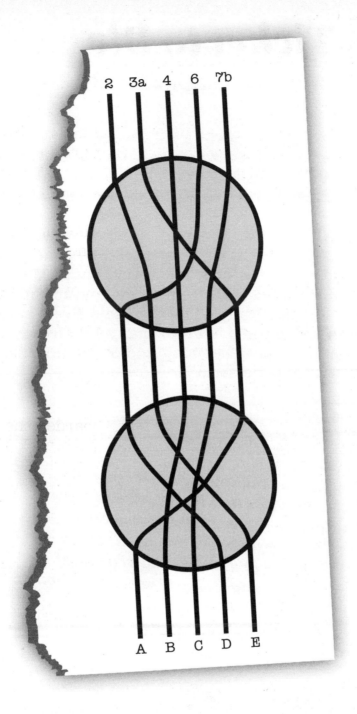

Which lettered location was the killer now heading towards?

_____

Ticket to Die

At Cross Purposes

Some days, I like to curl up with a good book by the fire, and other days I like to chase after steam trains with killers aboard. I rarely have the chance to indulge in the latter, so I rather enjoyed what happened next.

With the killer's destination established, it was time to intercept. I deduced that this could only be done at a level crossing, and asked the obliging station guard Mr Trackson for a map of the tracks. He handed me an incomplete map – somewhat apologetically – but then said I was sure to be able to fill in the gaps, given how many I'd already filled in for Graham. What a charming and observant man. Here are the instructions he scribbled down:

> Draw track pieces in some squares to complete a track that travels all the way from its entrance in the leftmost column to its exit in the bottom row. It can't otherwise exit the grid, and nor can it cross itself. Numbers outside the grid reveal the number of track pieces in each row and column. Every track piece must either go straight or turn a right-angled corner.
>
> Level crossings are in shaded squares.

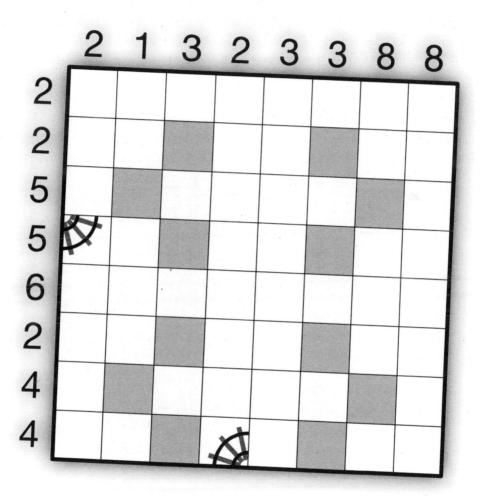

How many opportunities were there to intercept the train?

_____

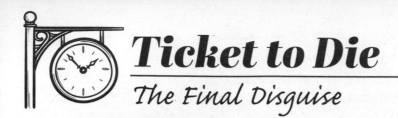
Graham rather graciously – and sensibly – suggested I go along with him to track down the train. It was only fair, as I seemed to be the only person who knew where it was going. We were given a photograph of the locomotive to look out for, which I thought would be a nice souvenir of the case for when I was back in Bishop's End.

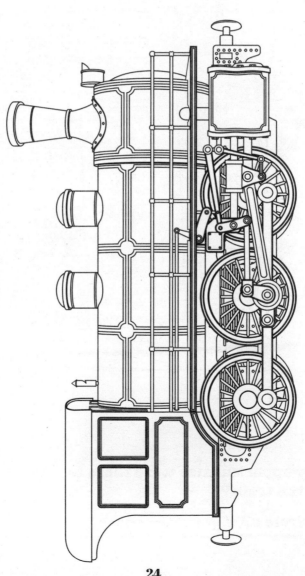

As we hot-footed it out of Flintchester station, Trackson the station guard ran up behind us to hand over a newer image of the train we were looking for. The locomotive in question had in fact been recently refurbished, and looked a little different to the first image. Stopping the wrong train would be a bad look, so we set about spotting the differences between the two.

To do: find all eight differences between the two locomotives

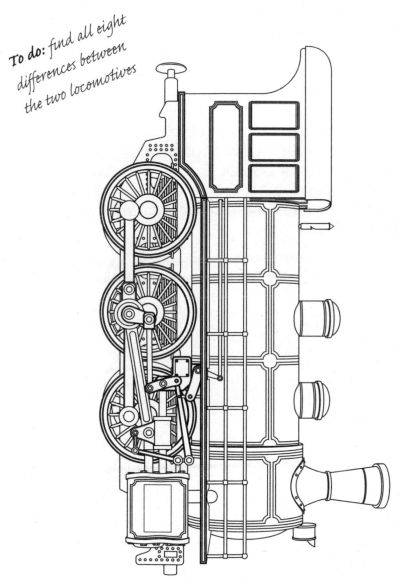

Can you circle all eight differences?

Ticket to Die

Time to Name Names

There's a certain thrill that comes from a ride in a police car – so long as you're in the front, of course. Graham and I sped after the train with its murderous cargo, and finally intercepted it at one of the marked crossings. Not wanting to draw too much attention to ourselves, we had a word with the train guard before we searched the train.

The guard usually tore each ticket in half and let a passenger keep one half as proof of purchase. A little unorthodox, but in this case handy: it seems our killer gave the guard both halves of his ticket to keep, presumably not wanting to be caught with any incriminating evidence.

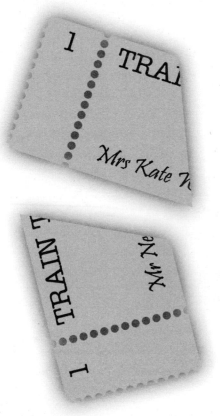

To do: find the only complete ticket amongst the halves to reveal the murderer's name

AIN TICKET

9lo Velazquez

1 | TRAIN

Dr Mar

Dr Her

TRAIN | 1

ille Franklin

TICKET

mah James

CKET

ICKET

isp

What is the murderer's name?

_____

Ticket to Die

Case Closed

After placing the two halves of the ticket together, we had our killer. Well, we had his name, and he was somewhere on the train with us. The charming but somewhat nonplussed train guard could not remember which of his passengers was the one who gave back both halves of the ticket, so he was of no further help. The polite but ineffectual Graham looked a little weary, and gave me a searching look – perhaps hoping I had some more answers for him. As luck would have it, I did.

Some years ago, after a string of particularly grisly murders in Bishop's End, I decided to make my own escape – and go on holiday, that is. I travelled all the way to Flintchester on a day very similar to today, and made my way to a well-reputed travel agent who, I was assured, would recommend to me the most fantastic places to see in Europe, and assist me in arranging a wholly fuss-free excursion on the continent.

When I arrived, it seemed I had been well advised. The young travel agent at whose desk I sat was full of tips and insider knowledge, recommending this and that hotel, such and such a rail company to look after me and even offering to make restaurant reservations for me before I set off. The cynic in me wondered whether he might be working on commission for these fabulous places but, nonetheless, he had put together a most inspiring itinerary.

When I left the travel agency, with all of the details ironed out, I asked the young agent for his name. I planned to write to his superiors and tell them how helpful he had been. He was more than happy to oblige, thanked me for my custom, and wished me a pleasant trip. I did indeed write to his superiors and, later, while I was actually *on* the holiday (somewhere near Lake Geneva), I wrote to the agent himself to thank him for organizing such a smashing vacation. In fact, I sent him a postcard.

So imagine my surprise when, years later, I held two halves of a train ticket bearing the very same name as the man who had sent me off to Europe. Had he really been responsible for sending a poor geography teacher to an early grave?

As it turns out, he had. I was able to identify our killer on the train after learning his name and – much to our surprise – he confessed to the murder on the spot.

Since my holiday to Europe, our killer had been promoted to the position of general manager of the travel agency, sending clients all over the world on fabulous excursions. All was well in business until about a year before the murder, when customers had begun to come into the agency with very specific requests.

There were hilltop towns they wanted to visit with which our agent had no ties, tiny restaurants so exclusive they could not be booked, and far-flung countries they wanted to travel to which, quite frankly, the modest agency had no business in whatsoever. Disgruntled clients came and went, having heard fantastic endorsements of unmissable foreign experiences, but leaving with only a sense of disappointment that they couldn't have such a trip organized for them.

Where were these superlative rumours coming from? What had caused this sudden uptick in desire for exotic holidays, well beyond the means of a Flintchester travel agency?

It transpired that the driving force behind all these recommendations was a young geography teacher by the name of Mr Norris who had undertaken all kinds of adventure and excursion during the long summer holidays. When the school pupils returned in September, they were told awesome tales of his travels to the Great Wall of China, the ruins of Machu Picchu, the cherry blossoms in Japan and the most exquisite pastries in all of Paris. There were photographs to look at too, taken by the man himself. Children told their parents of these spectacular travels, and in turn those parents with the means to travel abroad came straight to our killer to have their dreams realized – only to discover that such dreams could not be fulfilled.

After quizzing some of these would-be holidaymakers, the exasperated travel agent finally pieced together the source of all this foreign frenzy. Enraged by the undermining of his business, the agent decided to take a trip himself. He visited each of these fabulous places, one by one, to see if they were every bit as good as he had been led to believe and, to his dismay, they were.

Driven mad by the beauty of the world beyond Flintchester, he decided that the only way to restore the situation was not to expand his business and accommodate the wishes of his dreaming customers but rather, instead, to put a stop to the source of their desire. So he made plans to kill poor Mr Norris – whose only crime was a sense of adventure – and in so doing eliminate the problem once and for all.

And so he did. He sent Mr Norris postcards from his travels, warning the educator of his forthcoming demise. It seems that Norris had, however, succeeded in identifying the sender, as he had gone to Flintchester armed with the incriminating postcards. Had he planned a showdown at the travel agency? We may never know, since alas he did not leave the station alive. The killer accosted our doomed teacher on the station platform before fleeing on a nearby steam train as only a coward would do. As for Mr Norris, he stumbled into the waiting room clutching both his wounds and the incriminating postcards, before succumbing to his lethal injuries.

Needless to say, Graham – the police officer of questionable utility – looked rather relieved by the confession. In just one evening, a murderer had been hunted down and caught red-handed, with a confession to boot. It had been an ostensibly productive afternoon for him, with just the prospect of a little extra paperwork to keep him occupied. I, on the other hand, was three hours late for supper with the vicar and had, alas, somehow become separated from the new cheese grater which had coaxed me out of Bishop's End in the first place. Disaster.

Solving a murder is admirable, but were you paying attention to the other goings-on around Flintchester station? Test your powers of observation by answering the following questions:

1. What was the name of the station guard at Flintchester?

2. From where did I send my own postcard to the killer?

3. Whose sons did Mr Norris teach Geography to?

4. Which landmark did the killer visit in South Africa?

A BUMP IN THE ROAD

Another Case Solved by

Mrs Agnes Whitstable

A Bump in the Road

Bishop's End is just the right size for someone like me: not so big that you can't get around on foot, and not so small that you can't avoid your nosy neighbours when you absolutely need to. If I'm not walking I do have a very old motorcar that I bring out on special occasions – if I've just had my hair done, for example. The car is a rather wonderful shade of deep red that wouldn't look out of place in any decent winemaker's collection. Indeed, I nicknamed the car 'Claret' in my younger years, and it has rather stuck.

It runs quite well for its age – rather like myself, if I do say so – but every now and again I have to take the old car to the local garage to have it checked over and repaired if necessary. The proprietor is a rather brutish chap called Terrence Simpson, who charges rather a lot for his services but does more or less have a captive audience in Bishop's End. I was sitting in his garage one day as he began to reel off a list of extraordinarily expensive repairs for my car, when the sight of a young and somewhat baffled policeman caught my eye. I have an excellent nose for trouble.

The policeman in question – who later turned out to be the son of Chief Constable Snipping – was bringing in a car that looked more than a little worse for wear. The number plate was all in disarray, there were scratches all over the bottle-green exterior and there seemed to be, by the looks of things, a missing steering wheel. How they got it to the garage I will never know, but the tale young Snipping had to tell me was even more extraordinary.

The car had been stolen from right underneath the noses of the police – from the very police station car park, to be exact. One of the more observant secretaries saw though the station window that something unusual was going on among the parked cars, and had just put two and two together when this vehicle had finally screeched off. The car's owner, at that point, was somewhat of a mystery, but in any case the vehicle had not been known to the police until that moment.

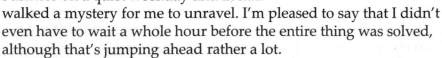

Well, of course, I could hardly believe my luck! There I was, minding my own business on a quiet weekday and in had walked a mystery for me to unravel. I'm pleased to say that I didn't even have to wait a whole hour before the entire thing was solved, although that's jumping ahead rather a lot.

You'll find my notes on the case here with some scribbles I made along the way – although I'll admit I should have guessed right from the start who exactly was the brains behind the whole thing. A bump in the road, indeed.

In solving this case, you'll need to find out the answers to the following questions:

1. **Where** was the car driven to after it was abandoned?

2. **What** was the original number plate?

3. **How** much would it cost to repair the damage to the car?

4. **Who** was the thief?

5. **Where** did the thief work?

You'll find my solutions at the back as usual, but keep an eye out for the unexpected: you may find you need some additional answers later!

Good luck,

Mrs Whitstable

A Bump in the Road

A Daring Escape

In a feat of incredible bravery – or spectacular stupidity – the vehicle was stolen from a spot right at the front of the car park of the local police station. Whoever had parked it there had left it for a long time, and someone clearly saw an opportunity to take it.

Fortunately, one of the constables thought it might be a good idea to track the speeding car. Here is the report he gave over the radio, with a map of the area opposite:

- From the police station (marked with a star), the car turned right onto the main road. It then took the third turn left, heading due north.

- From here it again took the third left towards some small streets organized in a grid. It continued to the end of the road, turned, and then took the third right.

- Still within the grid, the car then took the third left, and then turned right onto a main road.

- The car travelled north-east along the main road before taking the third right. It then carried on until it came to a junction with the main road and turned left, heading roughly east.

- The car passed two small streets on the right before immediately taking the third right, heading south-east towards another T-junction. There it turned left, and then left again at the next T junction.

- This main road was followed north, over an intersection with another main road before bearing left. They continued, passing another main road to the left.

- At a T-junction with an east-west main road, the car turned right and immediately left, and was then abandoned down a side street.

To do: *follow the police report and work out which of the four approximate locations, A to D, the car ended up in*

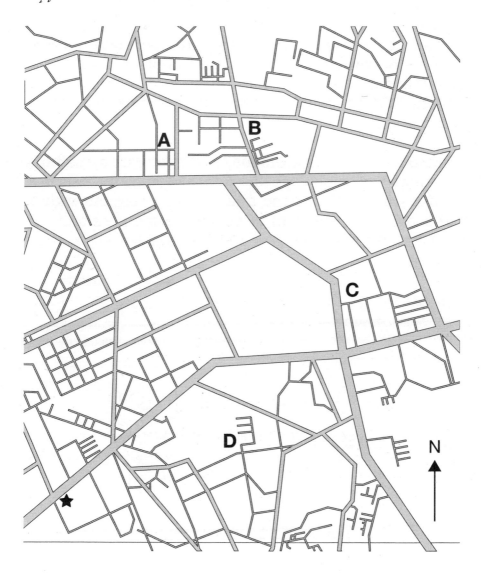

In which of the four approximate locations was the car abandoned?

_____

A Bump in the Road

Identifying the Problem

When the car was located, the number plate had been altered – presumably in a crude attempt to disguise it. Some parts of the letters and numbers had clearly been scratched off, though there was no evidence that any additional black markings had been added.

The constable was stumped, and brought the car into the garage for some repairs – where I encountered it for the first time. Spotting the altered plate (bottom right), I used a poster on the wall to suggest some possibilities for the original number plate – and found a helpful match.

To do: work out from the list of options what the car's original number plate must have been, using the official font guide

List of missing and stolen cars, with number plates:

BD64 DIG	FC37 OHJ
FO84 PDU	EO37 QTJ
HS51 OTQ	EQ84 ODU
FC31 CIU	EQ32 CIJ

Official font used on the original plate:

ABCDEFGHI
JKLMNOPQR
STUVWXYZ
1234567890

FO31 CI J

What was the original numberplate?

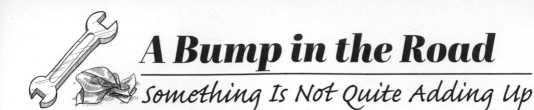

A Bump in the Road
Something Is Not Quite Adding Up

After determining the correct number plate, the car's grateful owner was brought to the garage to identify it. Her name was Alice Wallace, a charming young woman who works as a journalist for a local paper. She had inherited the car from her father but rarely used it, and thought that parking it in the police station car park would be a safe bet. I suppose, on a positive note, she would have an interesting story to write about at the end of all this.

Unfortunately, it was clear that several important parts of the car – such as its steering wheel – had been stolen by the thief. Alice looked rather upset, as well she might be, but Mr Simpson reassured her that he could replace all of the parts. Concerned about the cost, Alice was directed to a rather obscure pricing system on the wall behind Mr Simpson's desk. She would need one each of the items pictured.

I noticed that Mr Simpson had already drawn up an invoice for Alice – with incredible speed and foresight – but I thought it best to check he'd totted it up correctly.

To do: work out how much each of the replacement items cost, and then add up the total

40

Mr Simpson's Prices

No Negotiating

Invoice errors are your own

$$\text{🛞} = \text{🛢} \text{🛢}$$

$$\text{🛢} = \text{🔑} - £2$$

$$\text{💡} \text{💡} = \text{🛢}$$

$$\text{🔑} = \frac{\text{🛞}}{2} + £2$$

$$\text{🔑} \text{🔑} = £24$$

How much would Alice need to pay in repairs?

_____

A Bump in the Road
Printing Problems

Unlucky Alice paid for the repairs, and she and I had a nice chat while the paperwork was arranged: she was planning to bake a seven-tier cake for the village fête in a few weeks' time. We were in the middle of a deep discussion about buttercream when the police constable walked into the garage again, holding a steering wheel.

The wheel had been found on the street just behind the garage, and the constable had taken the liberty of dusting it for fingerprints in case it had come from a stolen car. Alice immediately recognized the wheel as coming from her own vehicle, which was a stroke of luck – the prints taken from it would surely help to identify the thief.

Shown below are four prints belonging to some of the more notorious residents of Bishop's End, and opposite are the partial prints found on the steering wheel. There was only one complete print among the fragments – belonging to the thief. I was rather pleased with how quickly I solved this particular puzzle, though I did have the head start of knowing that none of the fragments were rotated relative to the complete fingerprints below, and all fragments were the same scale.

Suzette Walker   Oliver Bruce   Terrence Simpson   Mark Pringle

Which whole fingerprint belongs to the thief?

_____

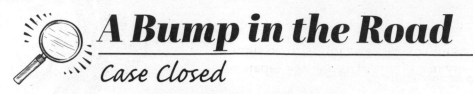

A Bump in the Road

Case Closed

When one is as observant as I profess to be, it's hard to be surprised by too many things in life. This case, however, was somewhat of a novelty to me: I was actually rather lost for words at the revelation of the thief's identity. It's rare, but it does happen.

What was uncovered that day was not a one-off crime of theft, but just one part of a much bigger scheme. The thief in question had no connection to Alice whatsoever, and this was not a targeted act of malice. Quite the contrary: this was a long-standing attack on the general community of Bishop's End. You can imagine how well I took the news.

The thief in question had, for many years, been stealing cars and car parts from under the noses of local people, though the vehicles were always found in conditions that meant they were not worth writing off just yet. Instead, they were taken to a Mr Terrence Simpson: the self-professed local expert who specialized in repairs and part replacements, charging a sum that befit his level of expertise. I realized, with some horror, that Alice was shortly to be charged an astronomical amount to replace her old steering wheel with her old steering wheel, which had been stolen from her earlier that very day. It would almost be genius, if it weren't so despicable.

Nobody likes to be made a fool of, even when one is in the privacy of one's home, battling with a particularly sticky crossword clue. This betrayal, however, felt like something else altogether. Although nobody had perhaps ever been effervescent with cheer when it came to doing business with this particular criminal, we had at least as a community decided to support his business at what was often great personal expense. The sense of disappointment was beyond words, although I had plenty of them for him too.

Speaking of expense, my bill was dutifully wiped clean with the arrest of the thief, and I was able to take my car home that day without forking out for the outrageously expensive repairs that the garage owner had just 'urgently' undertaken on my vintage vehicle. You'll not be surprised to hear that when I had it checked over a few months later by a more reputable mechanic, he found it to be running sweet as a nut with no signs of any need for replacement or repair.

At the end of it all, Alice did indeed have an excellent story to tell. She made the front page of the local paper – both as the victim and the journalist covering the story – and went into great detail about the scoop she had unwittingly been drawn into. I noticed in the write-up that rather a lot of the credit had been given to Snipping the Younger when it came to puzzling out the details of the case, but no matter. I was content with the rather flattering snapshot they had placed on the front page in which I was pictured, hair freshly done, in front of my trusty motor. Good old Claret.

Did you keep your eyes out for seemingly extraneous detail during your time solving this crime? Test your powers of observation by answering the following questions:

1. What was the last name of Bishop's End's Chief Constable?

2. What was the colour of the stolen car?

3. Who had Alice inherited the car from?

4. How many layers would be in the cake baked by Alice for the village fête?

THE FORCED HAND

Another Case Solved by

Mrs Agnes Whitstable

The Forced Hand

There are two inns in Bishop's End: The Hog and Badger and The Brass Buckles. My face is known in both of the establishments, and I would say they were more or less equal in both the quality of hospitality offered and the quality of customer. As such, I visit them both with restrained regularity and am always sure to see a friendly face whenever I do appear. The Brass Buckles, incidentally, does an excellent steak and kidney pie of a Thursday evening, although that is not, alas, how this story begins.

It begins instead with a group of people who caused an uncharacteristically violent scene on an otherwise peaceful winter's evening. The four friends – or, at least, they were friends at the start of the evening's proceedings – had been playing a game of cards in a corner of the room. They were regulars, and had apparently played hundreds of games of cards at that very table over the last decade or so. All of the games had been peaceful and unremarkable – until they were not.

There was, all of a sudden, a great skirmish in the corner of the room, and in the resulting fracas one of the card players attacked another of their own group. I had been sitting by the fire wrestling – figuratively – with an unusually cryptic crossword, and was quite lost in my own world until I heard the shouts and screams of other guests around me. I do sometimes wonder what anyone has to do to get a moment's peace in Bishop's End, but no matter: I decided I must get to the bottom of whatever was so important to these hot-headed players.

The fit of pique, it seems, had been brought on by an accusation of cheating in the game of cards they had been playing at that particular time. Curiously, none of the four players wanted to point the finger at the attacker, including the victim.

They were clearly horrified by how extraordinarily their game of cards had gone off the rails, and knew indeed that they were unlikely to be allowed back into The Brass Buckles ever again. One of them was also, at the very least, about to be arrested for their crime, no matter how much they each protested an unwillingness to participate in the investigation.

Despite their reluctance, I was able to put a pretty good picture of the events together before Detective Hancock, a friendly local police officer, turned up to arrest the attacker and give the rest of the group a stern talking to. Not as stern as I would have given, mind, but it was not really my place to jump in.

I've included the notes I took during the evening's proceedings, including a few hand-drawn sketches I'm rather proud of. You'll need them to unravel the facts of the event – and you'll be introduced to a few more reputable members of the Bishop's End community along the way. What a treat!

To solve the mystery of this unnecessary attack, you'll need to answer the following questions:

1. **What** weapon was used in the attack?

2. **What** was each of the players drinking?

3. **Who** was the attacker?

4. **How** had some of the players been cheating?

And again, keep an eye out for details which look out of place – there's likely to be a place for them somewhere!

Good luck,

Mrs Whitstable

The Forced Hand

The Glass is Quite Empty

In the ridiculous scuffle that ensued, one of the players was injured by a shard of glass. I didn't put it beyond this particular group to cause intentional injury during a card game, so I set about working out who had done the attacking. The fighting four were, understandably, asked to leave their table, but their fracas left a mess for me to examine in my own time. Usually I can't bear litter but in this case I was looking at a crime scene, so all's fair.

I noticed that each of the drinkers had been using a different style of glass, and that all four receptacles had been smashed during the incident. From the shards on the floor, however, I could see that one was missing: the shard which had been used to attack the cheating player.

Below are the four glasses as they should appear normally, and opposite is the untidy scene that was left on the floor of our normally serene public house. For ease, the shards are shown at the same scale and rotation as their completed counterparts, though I'm sure you'll still agree that the group left quite a mess. Tut tut.

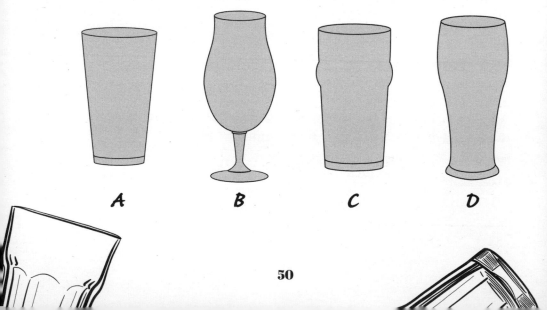

A   B   C   D

To do: piece together the shards of glass to establish which glass has a fragment missing

Which incomplete glass was used in the attack?

_____

The Forced Hand

To the Bitter End

After making sense of the mess on the carpet, I set about determining who had done the attacking. Whoever had been overcome with violent rage had used the shard from their own glass. I had just established which glass that must have been – but who was drinking out of it?

I asked around a few other patrons to see if they could determine who had been drinking what, but not everyone is as observant as me, it seems. I also asked the barmaid Hanna, who was understandably rather shaken – and so her memory wasn't complete either. Nevertheless, I rose to the challenge and still managed to establish what each of the disgraced players had been drinking, and from which glasses. Here's what I managed to find out:

To do: work out who was drinking from which glass, then use your knowledge of the missing shard to determine the attacker's identity

- Hanna said that Harold was drinking water, and Grace was drinking ginger beer

- Mrs Brindersley from number 42 said that whoever was drinking out of the glass with completely straight sides was drinking cider

- Paul from the Post Office said that Angela's glass had curved edges but definitely no ridge

- Harold was drinking from a glass with a stem, according to the couple at the table by the window

- Somebody was drinking bitter, but it wasn't Mortimer

- Seeing Paul reminded me to buy stamps, but that can wait

Who was the attacker?

_____

The Forced Hand

The Drama Unfolds

With the identity of the attacker established, I set about investigating the source of their ridiculous squabble. The attacker claimed that they had seen evidence of cheating from two of the other players: there had been some shuffling under the table, and the attacker thought that the two cheaters had been passing notes to one another, written on napkins.

As I approached the table once more I could see that napkins had indeed been used to communicate, but not in the way I expected. Instead of scribbled notes – which would have been undeniable evidence of foul play – one of the cheating players had devised an entirely different scheme. They had folded a square napkin in half, then in half again, and finally in half a third time, until it resembled a triangle. From here, they had torn away some of the resulting edges to create the shape shown opposite.

So far, so obscure, but I could see how the cheaters intended for their plan to unfold in this case: literally. When unfolded and restored to its original shape, I could see that the napkin's cutaway sections revealed a clue to two playing cards, which must have been crucial to the game. Crucial enough to attack a fellow player, at any rate.

Of course, I was not about to tamper with a crime scene with my bare hands, so I set about unfolding the napkin within the confines of my own head. I've included a guide opposite to show exactly how the square napkin had been folded, and the cut-out shape before it was unfolded.

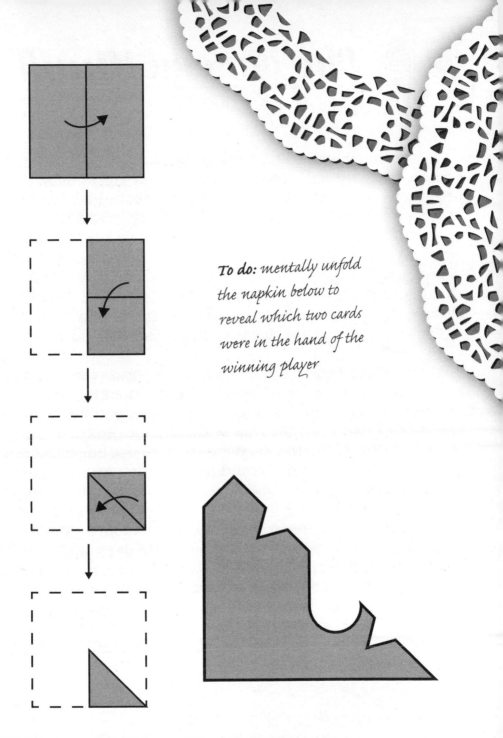

To do: mentally unfold the napkin below to reveal which two cards were in the hand of the winning player

Which two playing cards were indicated by the unfolded napkin?

_____

The Forced Hand

A Pack of Lies

I personally like to partake in the occasional game of bridge, but only with friends who I trust won't attack me after a hand doesn't go their way. My examination of the attacker's motive was purely for my own research, of course. I had already determined which of the four players was the perpetrator of the attack, and with that my work was done. Having also uncovered the means by which the cheaters planned to deceive their friends, I set about closing my investigation for the evening. It had been a ridiculous night, by all means, and I had had no supper.

Just before I went back to my table, however, I spotted something else rather unusual. Drinks, napkins and abandoned score sheets littered the floor, but the deck of cards they had been playing with largely remained on the table. Not all of the cards were face-up, but enough of them were visible that I could see another way in which some of these players might have been being duplicitous.

The group I had been investigating had clearly not been playing bridge, but all of the cards used that evening had been dealt from the same, single pack – the empty box of which was still on the table. Luckily, I didn't need any knowledge of card games to spot that something was amiss with whatever game they had been playing. Can you spot it?

To do: establish what is unusual about this pile of cards, all dealt from the same pack

What is unusual about the pile of cards?

_____

The Forced Hand

Case Closed

I decided to keep my most recent revelation to myself. After all, I had just established that at least two of the players were cheats, and one of the group had just perpetrated a violent attack. I thought it best not to try my luck. Nevertheless, I had concluded the important part of my investigations just as Hancock arrived, and was able to hand over the disturbers of the peace with a good chunk of evidence. I rather think Hancock and I make a good duo.

Thankfully the victim was largely unharmed, and after being attended to by Dr Missingtoe – a kindly if unfortunately named physician – was given a clean bill of health. The attacker was duly arrested, and the group of four players promptly barred from the The Brass Buckles indefinitely. You'd think that it would give me peace of mind that this kind of affray is now less likely to happen in the future, but you never do know what Bishop's End will come up with next.

The whole evening's debacle was frankly a terrible advertisement for card games and card players. I have no truck with gambling of any kind, and it's not difficult to see from this case that it brings out the worst in some people. The best you can ever hope for when gambling is an educated guess, and by now you'll have noticed that I much prefer cold, hard evidence.

After the clutter was cleared away and a relative calm returned to the inn, I sat back down at the fireside spot I had been occupying before the brawl. My crossword would be left undone for the day, but I was quite happy with the puzzles I had managed to solve in the meantime.

You may recall that I said this story did not start with an excellent pie by a crackling fire, but I'm thrilled to say it did end with one. It was Thursday, after all, and I thought I'd earned it. Bon appetit!

Well done for getting to the bottom of this cryptic crime. But were you paying attention? Test your powers of observation by answering the following questions:

1. How many people had been in the group playing cards?

2. Which drinks had the card players been drinking before the attack?

3. What is the name of the man who works in the Post Office?

4. How many visible cards were in the pile on the table in total?

A WHOLE NEW BALL GAME

Another Case Solved by

Mrs Agnes Whitstable

A Whole New Ball Game

In the summer months when the sun is high and the nights are short, you'd hope there would be less criminal activity to contend with. It's tempting to think that murky crime happens only under the cover of darkness, but that would be a mistake indeed; some of the most confounding crimes I have ever come across happened in broad daylight, in the warm summer sun.

This next case is such an example. I am pleased to report that there are no episodes of violence to contend with, though there is plenty of subterfuge, intrigue and forgery. These are naturally all things I would like to read about in a cosy armchair in the safety of my own home, but I live in Bishop's End, so this was bound to happen on my doorstep sooner or later. It is a blessing and a curse.

Bishop's End has some wonderful green spaces, including a wide sports pitch shared by various community clubs. There is a small pavilion, painted a rather blinding white, which is the headquarters of three different sporting groups: cricket, croquet and lawn bowls. Each sport as innocuous as the rest, or so I thought. As it turned out, the lawn bowls players had been engaging in some quite unsportsmanlike conduct: a spot of match-fixing.

I was in the habit of walking past the pitch on sunny days, often crossing paths with Mrs Walker, a friendly widow with a yappy dog called Ruffles. She was often keen for a chit-chat, but I'm afraid that of late I had found the unfolding drama so captivating that I had tended to ignore her friendly natter. Not so neighbourly as I usually liked to be, but I had a feeling I was about to uncover Bishop's End's latest scandalous secret. As if there hadn't been enough already!

The signs had been there for a long time. The group in question was the Bishop's End Lawn Bowlers, Old and Young, also known as the BELBOYs. The name was rather a misnomer, as there can't have been a single player under the age of 65, but I digress. As spring ripened into summer, I had noticed something not quite right with the group's performance. By all accounts they seemed to put in hours of practice in the warm sunshine, but were somehow never able to capitalize on their skills and win a competitive match – so I watched from the sidelines and did my very best to uncover the reason for their success, or rather the complete lack thereof.

I should say that this is a mystery I solved completely alone, without involving the police during the investigation. To accuse one's fellow villagers of a spate of match-fixing without a shred of evidence would be quite a social faux pas, not to mention terribly embarrassing in the unlikely outcome of my being incorrect.

To solve the mystery, it will help to uncover the answers to the following questions:

1. **What** pattern was being used to fix the matches?

2. **How** did the players communicate their plans to one another?

3. **In what way** did the group create false evidence of their results?

4. **Who** was the group's ringleader?

There will be other interesting snippets that crop up during the solving – there always are – so keep an eye out for anything which might come in handy in the future.

Good luck,

Mrs Whitstable

A Whole New Ball Game

A Sequence of Suspicious Events

I like to think that I'm not a busybody, but sometimes I cannot help myself, despite the players at the bowls club always seeming to be a cheerful lot. Many of them had retired early in their careers, which *would* make you rather cheerful, I suppose. Stopping by the pavilion one day, however, I spotted the score sheet from the team's away matches for recent months, and immediately saw something strange.

It's a wonder, really, that nobody had raised any suspicion before. The bowls club always seemed to lose their away games, despite spending several hours a week practising on the green. This seeming lack of prowess was belied by their away match scores, however, which showed a remarkable consistency and discipline, when looked at more closely.

The results sheet opposite shows only the number of points scored by the BELBOYs in each match, which was always played on a first-to-21-points basis. To test my theory that the matches were being fixed in a specific way, I used the partial results for June to predict the outcome of the final three games in June. If I turned out to be correct – and the games played out exactly as I had forecast – then we surely had a case of match-fixing on our hands. And that's just not cricket.

Well, you know what I mean.

To do: identify a pattern and establish what results will occur in the last three matches in June

Bishop's End Lawn Bowls Club: Away Matches

March results:
3 – 6 – 3 – 7 – 2 – 8 – 1 – 9

April results:
6 – 12 – 9 – 13 – 8 – 14 – 7 – 15

May results:
4 – 8 – 5 – 9 – 4 – 10 – 3 – 11

June results:
5 – 10 – 7 – 11 – 6 – ? – ? – ?

What 'should' the bowls team score in each of the last three matches in June?

A Whole New Ball Game

Tough to Pin Down

I waited for the three match results to come in, but I needn't have. Not to toot my own horn, but I had correctly surmised the pattern which the group were using to fix their losses. Their motive was yet to be established, so I hunted around for further proof.

Peering in through the pavilion windows, I spotted a noticeboard with the names of all twelve players on it. I had noticed that they moved the names around week by week, which I had presumed was to discuss tactics or to establish who should play in which teams. After a few weeks of observation – and definitely not nosiness – I realized, however, that the players had been using the noticeboard to further their subterfuge.

Each week, a different player was being identified as the one who should purposely lose an away match in some way – and the name of this week's loser had already been pinned onto the board. Luckily, I could see exactly how they were planning to trace it out. These fraudsters weren't so tough to pin down.

Team 1: James – Norah – John – Margot

Team 2: Victor – Clive – Barbara – Clara

Team 3: Ian – Bella – Gregory – Winifred

To do: use the team sheet and the noticeboard pins to reveal the name of the player who should purposely lose the next match

James

Clive

Norah

Clara

John

Victor

Barbara

Bella

Winifred

Margot

Ian

Gregory

Which player had been lined up to lose the next match?

A Whole New Ball Game

The Loser's Perspective

A little more snooping on my part led to a more scandalous discovery. I was sure now that the bowls players were deliberately losing their away matches, presumably for financial gain. There was a huge amount of betting among the bowling community in the county. Perhaps they needed the money, having retired early? Whatever was going on was surely not very sportsmanlike.

I was determined to put a stop to this once and for all, and hoped to add even more evidence to my case. Scattered on the table in the pavilion were four photographs – each showed a losing position, but in fact all were remarkably similar to a picture that I recognized from the Bishop's End Association Magazine (or the BEAM, as we call it), of which I had a copy with me. I could see that three of the images opposite were in fact altered versions of the original, providing more evidence of their fraudulent ways. Why fix their photos if they didn't have anything to hide?

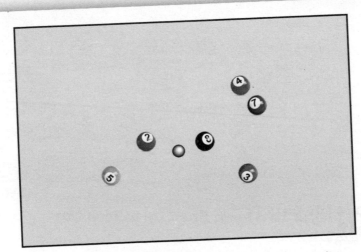

A losing game: The BELBOYs face up to another searing loss in the match against the Poppily St Martin's first team

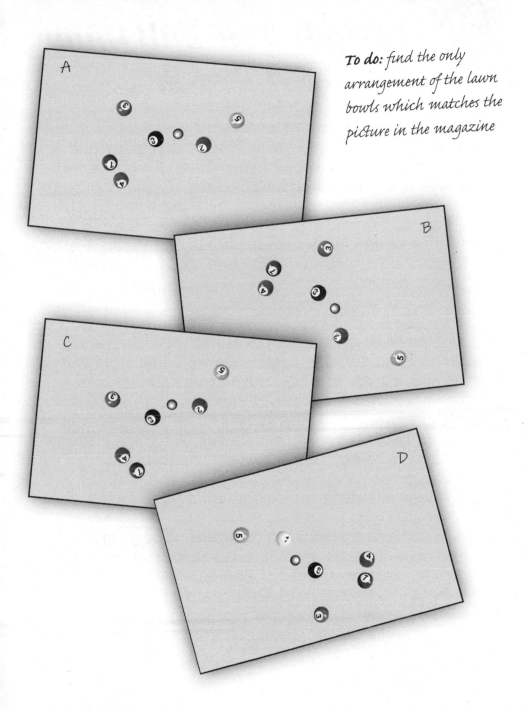

To do: *find the only arrangement of the lawn bowls which matches the picture in the magazine*

Which is the only photo that has not been altered?

A Whole New Ball Game

Time to Grass Them Up

By now I was certain of the group's cheating ways, and it was time to bring them down. The group surely had a ringleader, and I wished to unmask them. I had watched the players honing their skills for some weeks – although now I realized they were in fact practising how to lose a match without causing any suspicion, rather than to win. The promise of money can drive people quite mad, I notice. It strikes me as impressive that they could lose to an exact score for each match – they must in fact be highly talented, which seems deeply ironic!

I had narrowed my guesses down to three suspects: Bella, Gregory and Victor. Later that week, as I strolled past the bowling green with an ice cream (mint choc chip, an undisputed favourite), I saw the three of them 'training' for their upcoming games. They were playing a round robin game between themselves, with two players competing at once and the third player sitting out. Whoever won each match would stay on and play the person who was sitting out, and so on and so forth.

I made some notes on their progress, though was unable to note down every single result as my ice cream started to melt. I had surmised – correctly, it turned out – that the person to lose the final game of their practice session would be the ringleader. Game on. Or off, perhaps.

To do: work out who lost the final game of the nine, and therefore who the group's ringleader is

- Nine matches were played in total

- Gregory played exactly four games and lost all four

- Bella won the first four matches

- Bella beat Gregory three times

- Victor played in the sixth match

- Victor won three matches in total

Who was the group's ringleader?

_____

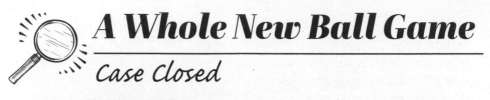

A Whole New Ball Game

Case Closed

I confronted the group's ringleader there and then. Well, I say confronted: I allowed them to finish their final match, and then waited for them to wander over to the pavilion, inside which the majority of the evidence was locked. I had briefly considered picking the lock so that I could wave the pictures at the group in a dramatic demonstration of my discovery, but thought it was best to maintain the upper hand, morally speaking. Plus, I had only just finished my ice cream, and didn't want to exert myself any more than necessary.

The ringleader looked a little nervous when they saw me waiting for them by the bright white door, and they were right to be: my deductions had been completely accurate. They were as guilty as the day was long, and – given we were approaching midsummer's day – the day was very long indeed.

The scheme had been going on for longer than even I realized, although I didn't reveal to the group that I had only been on their tails for the last month or so. The BELBOYs had been formed almost a decade previously by the very same ringleader, although it does seem that their first few years of conduct had passed without any nefarious incident. It was 'only' in the past five years or so that the temptation of match-fixing had reared its head, and the group had begun to implement their scheme.

Perhaps the greater crime here was not the breaking of rules, but the breaking of trust. The whole group of players had been complicit in throwing their matches to earn a little money from their competitions. There must have been teams all around the county that felt a sense of false superiority, always winning against a team whose players had such an apparent wealth of experience behind them and yet were never able to succeed when it counted.

I also realized – perhaps a little later than I should have done – that there must have been other equally crooked players in the leagues that the Bishop's End group had played, who knew of or even aided in the match-fixing. Indeed, perhaps there were several, scattered about the county conducting their mischief and rewarding those players who were more fussed about their wallets than the satisfaction of a fair game. This would at least explain why they worked so hard to lose to an exact score for each match, since it would permit anyone who knew of the match-fixing scheme to always predict an exact score, and thus win a maximum bet.

The group disbanded with immediate effect, I noticed, after I helpfully left the evidence contained in these pages on Hancock's desk at the end of a long, summer day. I had uncovered the truth, and the consequences were not for me to decide. I set off for home, feeling rather smug with my detective skills, with a vague mind to sign up to a taster session at the croquet club now that they had more time on the pitch. After all, how much trouble could one small village sports club get into, with me on the team?

Congratulations on uncovering a most unsporting scandal! Were you paying attention? Test your powers of observation by answering the following questions:

1. What is the name of Mrs Walker's dog?

2. In which month did my investigations take place?

3. How many players had their names on the pavilion noticeboard?

4. What flavour of ice cream is my undisputed favourite?

PAINTED INTO A CORNER

Another Case Solved by

Mrs Agnes Whitstable

Painted into a Corner

Most of us in Bishop's End lead a relatively modest life, so standing out from the crowd is not something we take to easily. Among the bungalows and tidy gardens, however, there is a rather magnificent manor house called Butternut Hall. The exterior of the house is quite imposing, with large windows and the occasional turret, but the owner of the house is not. His name is Oscar.

Oscar Montague has lived at Butternut Hall for many years, and he is known as a friendly, if a little eccentric, resident of Bishop's End. He is a collector of modern art pieces, and tends to show off his collection to guests at an annual festive party which I never fail to attend. I should note that this is less to do with the art and more to do with the tremendous vol-au-vents that are usually passed around, although Oscar doesn't need to know that.

But back to the story. I received a message from Oscar several years ago, denoting that he was in a serious state of distress. One of his newest masterpieces – and incidentally the most valuable – had gone missing in the middle of the night. After padding around the house forlornly searching for any sign of an intruder, Oscar was resigned to the fact that whoever had taken the painting must have been someone he knew, as they had used a key to let themselves in.

I privately felt that Oscar was far too naïve, trusting his family enough to give each of them a key, but it seems it was a reciprocal arrangement. And although friendly with most of his kin, I believe there had been some bitterness when Oscar inherited Butternut Hall in the first place. Obviously there was no justification for theft, but the ill feeling would be a good place to begin the inquiries in any case.

I trundled over to Butternut Hall on a chilly winter's morning and set about solving the mystery of the missing masterpiece. It turned out that Oscar was correct that the thief was indeed plucked from his own family tree, but the case still managed to throw up plenty of unexpected twists and turns along the way.

I'm pleased to say that we did eventually recover the stolen artwork and expose the recalcitrant relative before the masterpiece came to any harm. I personally wasn't sure that this particular piece had been worth all the fuss, but that is none of my business. I have an eye for crime, not abstract art.

Oscar and I are old friends, but I note that he'll tell people that we solved the mystery together, although I think you'll see that I did most of the mental heavy lifting in this case. He did of course supply a lot of the evidence, being the chief victim and witness, so perhaps I am just splitting hairs – or heirs, in his case.

To solve the mystery yourself, it will help to gather the answers to the following questions:

1. **Which** family members could be ruled out of the investigation?

2. **By what route** did the thief escape with the masterpiece?

3. **Who** was the thief?

4. **Where** did they hide the masterpiece?

You know the drill by now: leave no stone unturned, and keep a note of anything interesting you find along the way. You never know when you might be called to an interview yourself!

Good luck,

Mrs Whitstable

Painted into a Corner

All in the Family

Oscar was keen not to cast undue aspersions on his own family members, despite knowing that one of them had clearly stolen a valuable artefact from him. He was, however, able to rule out several suspects for me, narrowing down the search rather a lot.

I've included his family tree opposite, which was framed in the hallway of his magnificent home. Needless to say, he realized that he now needed to reduce the number of these who could continue to hold a key to his house.

Quotes taken directly from Oscar Montague:

- Only my paternal grandmother is still alive, out of all my grandparents

- My cousin lives in Australia with her mother, so it can't have been them

- My nephew is too young to have committed the crime, as is his younger brother

- My sister-in-law and her children were abroad when the theft took place, so it can't have been them

- My mother is above suspicion, as is my brother-in-law

- It can't have been either of my grandmothers' sons-in-law

- Jane said her niece was visiting at the time, so it can't have been her either

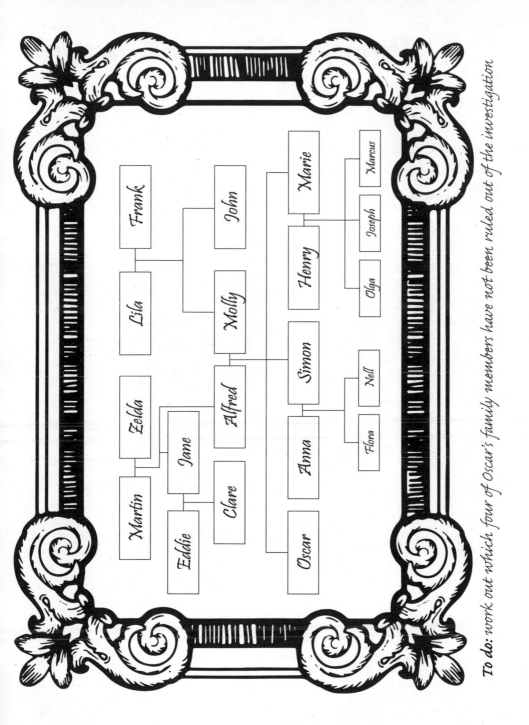

To do: work out which four of Oscar's family members have not been ruled out of the investigation

Which four family members are the prime suspects?

_____

Painted into a Corner

A Labyrinth of Lies

Oscar's manor was laid out in a rather complex way, with several staircases between the two floors and a maze of corridors between them. Whoever stole the painting had travelled between the two open doors on the ground floor – the only ways to enter and exit the building. I've included the floorplans here, with the staircases numbered.

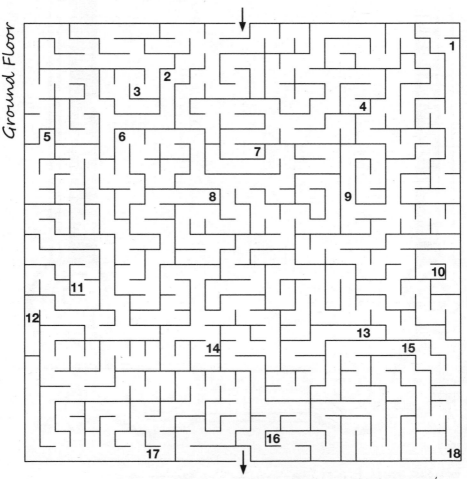

To do: find the thief's route from the entrance at the top of the ground floor to the exit at the bottom, and work out how many flights of stairs were climbed and descended in total during the escape

Each staircase gave the thief the option of travelling up or down between floors to the same number on the other floor, or carrying on straight past it. Oscar noted that the staircases are steep and narrow, and claimed that any relatives older than him wouldn't have been able to go up or down them more than three times in total. So if the thief took a staircase-heavy route then we could rule out some suspects. I pointed out that his family's ages were not on the tree, but he observed: 'Not to worry. I'm the eldest of my siblings, and both my parents were younger than their siblings.' It was time to narrow it down. Assume the thief did not retrace their route at any time.

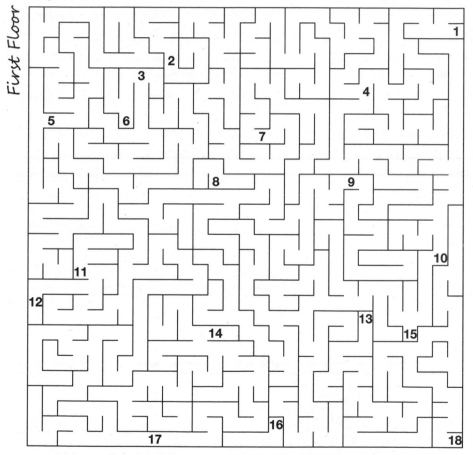

Which additional family members can be ruled out as suspects, if any?

_____

Painted into a Corner

A Note of Panic

With a small number of suspects remaining, Oscar had drawn a blank. I, too, was unsure how to proceed, though I decided not to let that show. Instead I suggested a nice cup of Earl Grey while we reflected on the latest revelations.

Fortunately, we were interrupted in the best possible way while waiting for the tea to brew, when Oscar received a letter in his sister's handwriting. We decided to trust the contents of it, which spelled out the situation a little more clearly. It seems his sister did not want to be caught telling tales on one of her own family members, so she had concealed information quite stealthily within the message.

Despite her disguise, I managed to spot the thief's name more or less immediately – and that was before I'd even taken a sip of the restorative cup of tea. Quite impressive, I thought.

To do: use the note, and the clues it gives, to determine the name of the thief

Only two suspects remain, apparently –
and I wanted to give you a helping hand

Look very closely at this note, and make
sure your investigations go back to the
very beginning

Go carefully from now on – your thief
hid themselves quite well at the start

A little hint: I've named the thief in this
message, sorry for the initial confusion!

Who does Oscar's sister name as the thief?

_____

Painted into a Corner

Pull the Other One

We had the name of our prime suspect, and Oscar was keen to confront them. We travelled over to the thief's family home, and were surprised to find it apparently empty. Oscar produced a key and let us in, saying that he knew already where the stolen artwork would be hidden.

He knew there was a secret room in the house, hidden behind a bookshelf. The door could only be opened by taking out the correct 'key' book; taking out the wrong one would set off a series of alarms. Unfortunately, Oscar could not recall exactly which book he needed, but luckily he remembered enough of the information about the key book that I was able to puzzle it out for myself.

The key book is either marked with a square number, or is immediately next to a book with a square number

The key book isn't marked with a cube number

The key book's number is divisible by 3

After the above eliminations, the key book's number is the highest in value of the remaining options

To do: use the clues to determine which of the numbered books should be pulled to reveal the hidden door

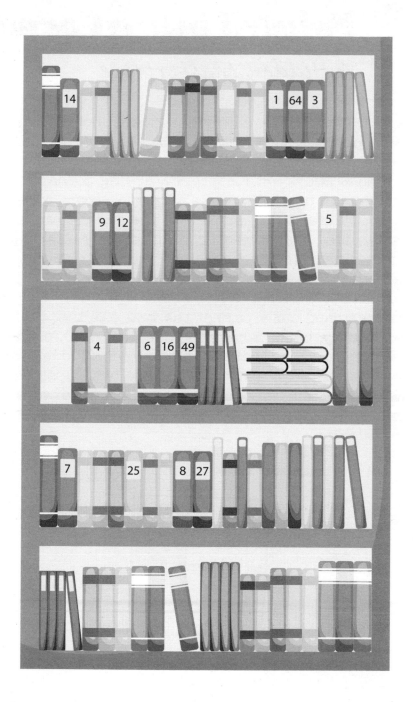

Which numbered book opens the secret door?

_____

Painted into a Corner

A Hidden Masterpiece

The door swung open into what looked like a cross between a private study and an art gallery. It seemed very much like the thief had been planning to replace their looted artwork with a forgery, hoping perhaps that Oscar might not notice. Placed around the room were four paintings that were very similar to the stolen painting – so much so, in fact, that it was not immediately clear which was the original. Luckily, however, it turned out that the original had not been altered at all.

Oscar sketched out a part of the real painting that he recalled exactly, which I have included below. Opposite are the four canvases that sat in the thief's hidden room. Some of the paintings appeared to have been upside down or perhaps even sideways on, so the section we were certain of might have been rotated, relative to each of the four paintings.

To do: use the sketched section from the image to determine which is the correct painting from the four canvases shown

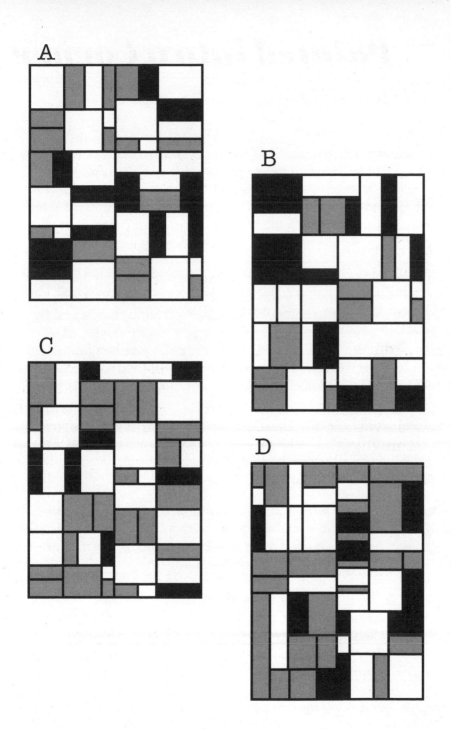

Which is the real masterpiece?

Painted into a Corner

Case Closed

We had found the masterpiece, but not the thief who took it. Yes, we had the name of the criminal, but their physical whereabouts were a mystery. I doubted they might ever be found, if they didn't want to be: the whole Montague family seemed to live in homes which were full of mazes and hidden rooms. I half expected to be shown a door with a secret tunnel that led me to an underground palace, but no such luck. They would be excellent houses for a game of sardines.

While I was lost in my ponderings about the best possible hiding places in Butternut Hall, the suspect themselves walked into the secret study. The house had not been empty at all, it seems, and the sneaky relative had predicted we would go straight to where the stolen treasure had been stashed. To be honest, I was beginning to wonder whether the thief's heart was really in it: their identity had not been too tricky to uncover, and nor were the stolen goods.

As it turned out, the thief had indeed begun to feel some regret at their actions, not least when they discovered that they didn't have a criminal's instinct for covering their tracks. Seemingly reluctantly, they told us their great secret: they were a huge fan of modern art.

I have to admit that Oscar and I were both taken aback just a little at this revelation. It was not really a question of taste, but a question of logic: why would you endanger a priceless piece of abstract art if you were truly such a self-declared aficionado?

I think the answer to that lies in the fact that the thief was not being entirely forthcoming. They planned to travel to the continent to study art for themselves, but knowing the financial value of the masterpiece they had decided to take it and sell it, using the profits to fund their studies – and to travel in some considerable style.

The reason behind the forgeries in front of us was simple: they were planning to replace the real painting with a copy of their own, and hope that Oscar might not notice. Based on how easy it was to spot the fakes from the real masterpiece, I might be tempted to say that our young thief still had a lot to learn from Europe's finest painters.

Oscar decided not to press charges on this occasion; the painting was returned to its rightful place at Butternut Hall, and nobody was arrested for the crime. I had to admit I was rather disappointed with the outcome; it seemed rather an anticlimax after we had spent the morning piecing together the investigation.

All was not lost, however. Oscar thanked me for my help and sent me on my way with a box of breakfast croissants as a gesture of gratitude. Say what you like about the man, he has an excellent pastry chef somewhere. Criminally tasty.

A quick pat on the back for your detective efforts... but were you paying attention? Test your powers of observation by answering the following questions:

1. What delightful food was passed around at Oscar's annual festive party?

2. What is the name of Oscar's maternal grandmother?

3. How many shelves were on the bookcase door to the thief's hidden room?

4. How many forged paintings were in the hidden room?

THE WRITING ON THE WALL

Another Case Solved by

Mrs Agnes Whitstable

The Writing on the Wall

It's not every day that a celebrity comes to Bishop's End, but when it does happen it can cause quite a stir. We've had the occasional renowned botanist come and judge the vegetable competition, and even once a Hollywood movie star drank at The Hog and Badger (having got lost, we think, on the way to a golf course). But no famous person made quite as much of an impression as the renowned crime writer Marjorie Winkleman. Not least because she was murdered in the library that very same day.

News of her literary tour had reached us several months before her visit, and the residents of Bishop's End were abuzz with the thought of meeting the esteemed author. She had written dozens of books during her long career, and the Bishop's End Library had a copy of every single one. The tour coincided with the release of her latest novel, and she had agreed to visit the library to give a talk on her career, and to sign copies of her books for the librarygoers. In the day's schedule were to be tea and biscuits, questions and answers, and perhaps a photo opportunity for the lucky attendees. For the unlucky novelist, however, all that occurred was her untimely death.

Being a fan of Mrs Winkleman's work, I made sure I had a front row seat for the event – not knowing, of course, that I was about to become a key witness in her murder. I usually have very little truck with celebrities, but I have to admit that the author had become somewhat of a hero to me. Her keen observation of human habits and her drive to leave no stone unturned in her mysteries are qualities I try to emulate in my own detective work. I was, for want of a better word, rather giddy at the thought of meeting her.

As well as being an esteemed author, Marjorie Winkleman was noted as being somewhat of an eccentric character. It was rumoured that, after so many years of crafting grisly and fictitious murders for her avid readers, she had become rather paranoid. Danger, apparently, was everywhere. In her memoir, she had written that she made sure to never sign her autograph in the same way twice, and even reserved a separate signature for official documents, lest someone try to copy it and use it for nefarious purposes.

By all accounts she was a little nutty, but I rather think it all added to the excitement of her visit. Indeed, she had us all checked for weapons before we entered the library, which seemed a little extreme. The only offensive item uncovered during the search was an overdue library book that accompanied Mrs Sanderson, the postman's wife. Tut tut.

On the day of the visit, a kind of quiet frenzy settled over the attendees queueing to enter the library. After a little shuffling and some frankly poor-natured elbowing, we settled down in our rows and, at long last, the author appeared to a smattering of applause. Moments later, she would be dead. In the furore and horror that followed the moment of murder, I gathered my wits about me and set about solving the crime – for it was abundantly clear that this was a premeditated act of malice. Not to pat myself on the back too much, but I'm pleased to announce that I solved the case that very afternoon. Can you?

On the following pages are my notes and observations from the day in question. To solve the mystery, you'll need to establish answers to the following questions:

1. **What** warning message was left for the victim?

2. **Where** had the murderer hidden themselves?

3. **What** did the killer look like?

4. **What** was the murderer's name?

5. **What** was the murderer's motive?

And, as always, keep your eyes peeled for unusual tidbits of evidence while you solve. You never know what might come back to help you – or haunt you!

Good luck,

Mrs Whitstable

The Writing on the Wall

A Handy First Clue

Despite the serious nature of her books, Marjorie Winkleman clearly knew how to have a good time. Before the attendees of the book signing were seated in the library, we were each given a small piece of paper with a puzzle on it. The puzzle was intended to help us pass the time as we waited for her arrival, though naturally I completed mine in moments. Clues are my speciality.

The puzzle had apparently been designed by Marjorie herself, and instructions for completing it were printed on the back – which I have included below. The objective was to reveal a hidden image which, according to the famed writer, would indicate what was often a key piece of evidence in a crime. This would certainly prove to be true in the subsequent investigation.

Shade some squares according to the given clue numbers.

The clues provide, in reading order from left to right or top to bottom, the length of every run of consecutive shaded squares in each row and column.

There must be a gap of at least one empty square between each run of shaded squares in the same row or column.

Happy Solving!

To do: *follow the printed instructions to reveal what Marjorie Winkleman considered to often be a key piece of evidence*

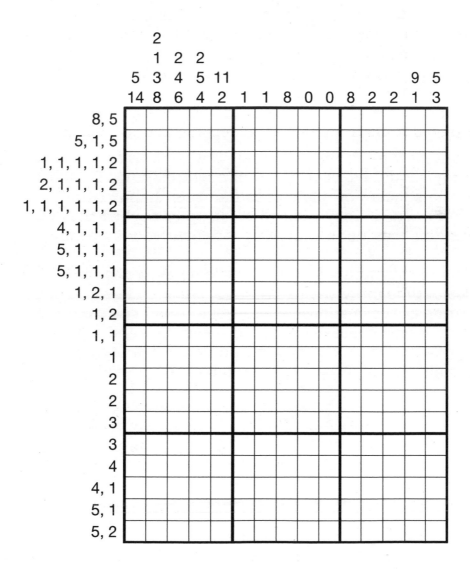

What type of evidence does the puzzle suggest?

_____

The Writing on the Wall

A Sticky End

Not to pat myself on the back, but I finished my puzzle rather earlier than the other attendees. Looking around, an unevenly stacked pile of books caught my eye, as shown in the contemporaneous photo, opposite.

The stack of books were all works by Marjorie Winkleman, which had been set aside for her to sign for her doting fans in Bishop's End. The book titles were all as they should be, but even at a slight distance I could see that the stickers on the spines had been handwritten and recently added. They seemed so sloppily applied that I felt something was not stacking up – figuratively speaking.

The photograph would later become evidence for the police, although by then I had long since understood the meaning of these adhesive additions. I had realized that these stickers concealed a coded message – and not one left by a librarian, but by a killer. Sadly it was only in hindsight that I spotted the warning they provided.

To do: use the numbered stickers to reveal a hidden warning message from the killer

What warning message had been spelled out?

_____

The Writing on the Wall

In The Bad Books

At long last Marjorie Winkleman appeared, and took a seat in front of her audience. Ready to begin her talk, she sat down and drew breath – not knowing that it would be her last. Before she could say a word, a copy of her latest novel fell from the ceiling, struck her square on the head, and killed her. Quite a turn-up for the books.

The book had been suspended in the air on the decorative flags which usually pointed librarygoers to different sections of the library. Whoever had set up the fatal trap had clearly severed the chain of flags from wherever they had concealed themselves, releasing the deadly book and the network of flags along with it.

The system for organizing the books is given below, and opposite is a photograph of the flags as they landed after falling from the ceiling – the 800s section is shown on top.

Books can be found in the following sections:

000 – 099: Computer science and general works
100 – 199: Philosophy and psychology
200 – 299: Religion
300 – 399: Social sciences
400 – 499: Language
500 – 599: Pure science
600 – 699: Technology
700 – 799: Arts and recreation
800 – 899: Literature
900 – 999: History and geography

To do: *work out which section of the library the killer was hiding in, based on the severed chain in the photograph*

In which section of the library was the killer standing?

_____

The Writing on the Wall

Ways and Means

It seemed likely that our murderer was a resident of Bishop's End – a horrifying thought for those of us who must have rubbed shoulders with them over the years. They clearly had knowledge of the ins and outs of the library, and had revealed as much in their coded message to Mrs Winkleman. Taken literally, the cryptic comment on the stack of books suggested that, due to its labyrinthine layout, options for exiting the library were limited.

(In a more artistic reading of the message, I mused, the killer might have been deliberately hinting at the poor writer's impending death – though it was not the time to muse on the linguistic prowess of a cold-blooded killer.)

Working on the assumption that my first interpretation was correct, I set about trying to find out how the killer must have exited the library. Based on my years of experience as a library user I was able to draw up a quick floorplan, which I have included opposite. Given that all of the attendees, including the killer, had been ushered in through – and were subsequently blocking – the main entrance, there was only one option for an exit.

To do: work out which of the labelled exits shown opposite was used by the murderer to escape the library

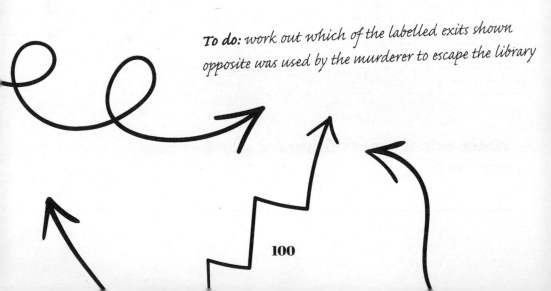

Which exit did the murderer escape through?

_____

The Writing on the Wall

Four Ways to Spot a Killer

I rushed outside – as fast as an elderly detective can rush – using the exit the killer must have taken. Knowing that the perpetrator could not be far away, I spoke to several people in the vicinity, and asked if they had seen anyone come by recently. Between them, they identified four different suspects. One witness had seen someone pass by with a pair of large scissors – it was our killer, fresh from the scene of the crime.

The witnesses gave some helpful descriptions, although none of them was quite complete. Each of the four people spotted had distinct hair and a distinct colour of jumper, and they were each carrying a different object. They were also all travelling in different ways, such as on foot or by bicycle. Luckily, my skills of deduction meant that I was able to quickly establish the appearance and locomotive method of the killer.

To do: work out the killer's hair colour, jumper colour, mode of transport and what they were carrying from the witness statements

Witness A:
- Saw a bald person running
- Saw a blonde person wearing a jumper the same colour as one of the other suspects' hair, but not their own hair

Witness B:
- Saw a brown-haired person walking
- Saw a person with a blue jumper carrying a newspaper
- Saw a red-haired man cycling past

Witness C:
- Saw a cyclist carrying a baguette
- Saw a person in a purple jumper carrying scissors
- Saw a person travelling by motorbike carrying a handbag

Witness D:
- Saw a man in a green jumper riding a bicycle
- Saw someone running in a blue jumper
- Saw someone wearing a brown jumper

What did the killer look like?

_____

The Writing on the Wall

The Seal of Disapproval

Not having yet caught the killer, I made my way back to the library to examine the scene of the crime. Each of the stamps shown here had been inked into the library's newest Marjorie Winkleman novel – that is to say, into the murder weapon.

The librarygoers of Bishop's End are a fastidious people: we like to do things by the book. The novel had been in huge demand as soon as it became available, and the library has a very strict policy about how long one may borrow a book for. The residents always hold on to their newest read for as long as possible, and, naturally, nobody had returned it before they absolutely had to, without actually returning it late.

One of these stamps was an odd one out – and I suspected it was forged by the murderer.

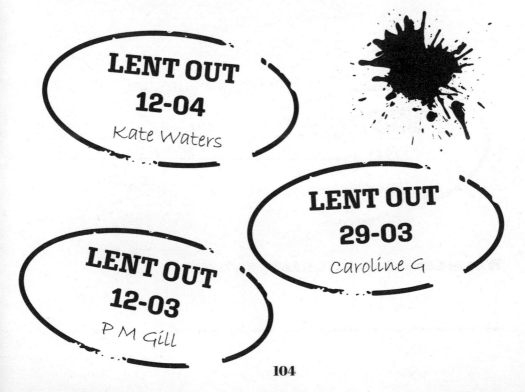

LENT OUT
12-04
Kate Waters

LENT OUT
29-03
Caroline G

LENT OUT
12-03
P M Gill

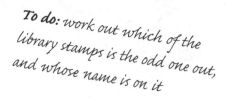
To do: work out which of the library stamps is the odd one out, and whose name is on it

LENT OUT
01-03
Mrs A Walker

LENT OUT
15-03
Miss T Peck

LENT OUT
22-03
Dr Smith

LENT OUT
05-04
Mr M Grant

LENT OUT
08-03
S Wren

Whose name is on the odd stamp out?

_____

The Writing on the Wall

A Signature Move

We had our killer. I swallowed down some personal disgust at the revelation in ink: we may have had an actual murder on our hands, but forging a library stamp felt like a step too far. Nonetheless, I tracked down the person whose name was revealed on the irregular record, and confronted them with my accusation of murder. I could see that they had the means and opportunity to kill the poor author – but what was their motive?

By way of a response, the killer showed me the following signatures, all from their own personal Winkleman collection. Given what we already know about Marjorie's unusual signature style, something struck me as odd about these autographs.

To do: examine each of the signatures and compare them against one another to reveal an inconsistency – given what you know about the victim's signature style

What is unexpected about this collection of Marjorie Winkleman's signatures?

_____

The Writing on the Wall

Case Closed

Our killer, it seemed, was the greatest Marjorie Winkleman fan of all – he had collected all of her books, including some priceless first editions, and read every tale from cover to cover. He had idolized the author, admiring the improbable lack of plot holes in her twisting, turning narratives. She seemed, on the surface, to be one of a kind; a rarity, a unique gem of a writer never to be repeated. Unfortunately for Marjorie, it would be a *lack* of uniqueness that would land her in hot water with a murderer.

Every single one of the killer's books had been signed at one point or another by Marjorie Winkleman and, as was her way, each autograph had been unique. She was, as I said, famed for her idiosyncratic ways – and perhaps her touch of paranoia – and had always gone to great lengths to ensure that her signatures each differed from one another. There would be no way to prove it, really, but the chances were that she was unlikely to ever exactly recreate her own autograph like-for-like. Indeed, how many times do you think you've ever exactly duplicated your own signature? I'd wager none.

The odds, however, were not on her side – in more ways than one. Our killer had recently bought a copy of Winkleman's latest bestseller: the very novel that would kill her off, although she wasn't to know. The murderer had written to Marjorie herself, hoping to obtain an early copy, and was rewarded with a hot-off-the-press edition complete with her prized signature. The killer's joy turned to horror, however, when he saw the coveted autograph and realized he had seen it before. Hurriedly, he compared the new signature against all of those in the books he already had and, lo, there was a match. And on his own bookshelf, would you believe.

Hero worship is a dangerous game, and the killer was driven mad by the idea that his idol might be anything less than he expected of her. Not only that, but he felt that his own personal collection of her books had changed from priceless to worthless in an instant. Knowing that she would be coming to Bishop's End in a few weeks' time, he set up an elaborate plan to bring her life's work crashing down around her – quite literally – in an act of ruthless and bizarre revenge.

So far, so absurd. No matter how many motives I stumble across when investigating a criminal case, I have still never happened upon one which could justify the act of murder. My disdain must have been apparent as I questioned the killer, but never more so than when we came to the matter of the forged stamp. What on earth had been his thinking there?

The killer was ready with his answer. From his fanatical reading of Winkleman's canon, he had surmised that his own fingerprints might well be the piece of evidence which brought his downfall when the crime was investigated. Knowing that he might struggle to remove his prints from the weapon in a hurry, he instead decided on a feat of misdirection. The plan was to give the impression that he had simply taken out the novel as an innocent customer of the library at an earlier date. Any fingerprints on the book, therefore, could simply have been explained away by his apparent borrowing.

The killer seemed rather pleased with his strategy, and even more so when he noted that Marjorie herself had pointed out his logic with a puzzle of her own that very day. His own downfall came, however, when he assumed that the readers of Bishop's End were any less fanatical than he. Each of the devoted readers had taken out their books for exactly the amount of time they were allotted, and not a day less. It's something that might easily have been predicted knowing the habits of these inhabitants, though I prefer proof. As it happens, I had been trying to borrow the book myself ever since it was released, only to be told that every single time the book had been returned, it was lent out again the very same day. Thus, when I saw the stamps, I knew that something was out of place.

Our killer, too wrapped up in his own ridiculous despair, had failed to notice that there were other readers just as dedicated to his heroine as he, and it was their devoted habits that led me straight to him. Apparently he did not share Winkleman's keen eye for observation after all.

As discussed, my name was not one of those on the stamped pages of the Bishop's End library book, and that particular copy is, as you might suspect, now out of action. I eventually made the long journey to Flintchester to borrow it, at great inconvenience. One might think that solving the poor author's murder might have entitled me to a free edition of my own, but alas, no.

It is only now that I look back at the case that I see how deeply ironic the title of her final novel was:

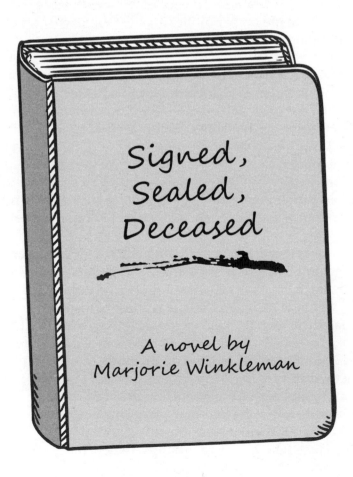

Signed, Sealed, Deceased

A novel by Marjorie Winkleman

Solving a murder is admirable, but were you paying attention to the other goings-on around the library in Bishop's End? Test your powers of observation by answering the following questions:

1. In which Bishop's End establishment was a Hollywood movie star spotted?

2. How many books had been set aside in a stack for Marjorie Winkleman to sign?

3. Who was the first person to take out the new Marjorie Winkleman book in the library?

4. Which numbered section of the library was dedicated to literature?

A DRAMATIC ENDING

Another Case Solved by

Mrs Agnes Whitstable

A Dramatic Ending

You have probably noticed by now that life is almost never dull in Bishop's End – if you're me, anyway. There seems to be drama everywhere I turn, as well as life's more regular comedies and tragedies, and so I never feel the need to go to the theatre. A few years ago, however, there must have been a quiet period in the criminal calendar, so I decided to take a trip to the village hall to see the local amateur dramatics group in their latest production.

According to the other residents, these evenings could be counted on to provide a bit of harmless fun. The quality of acting was not such that it might trouble the stars of London's West End, but the Bishop's End Amateur Dramatic Society (or the BEADS, for short) were a competent enough troupe. The play to be performed was billed as a comedy, which suited me just fine. What unfolded next, however, was a tragedy of the worst kind.

I had largely been persuaded to attend the show by the claims that tubs of vanilla ice cream were available to purchase during the intermission, which seemed like a good attempt at recreating the thrill of the theatre in our humble village hall. Alas, the promised goods were never produced, as one of the show's leading ladies was killed just offstage in the opening act. Harmless fun it was not.

Whoever had killed the poor girl was a member of the BEADS, and was performing in the very play we had begun to enjoy that evening. After a piercing scream followed the discovery of the poor victim, however, no one immediately claimed to know the identity of the killer. Either the surviving actors were too afraid to point the finger of blame at one of their cast-mates, or they truly did not know who the killer was. Enter Agnes Whitstable, stage left.

As the schedule for the evening changed from merriment to murder, I set about determining who had committed the heinous crime. I don't usually like to have an audience while I conduct my investigations, though in this case I had no choice. I did my best to keep a low profile for the opening scenes of the solve, and even managed to piece together parts of the puzzle from the comfort of my chair.

The members of the audience were, fortunately, above suspicion, as we had been sitting rather obediently in our rows of chairs under the watchful eye of the steward George Hillock. I say steward, but he was only moonlighting as one for this evening. His day job was herding sheep out beyond Flintchester, although I supposed there might be some similarities in the two roles.

Even if I say so myself, this particular case was wrapped up in record time. With the help of a friendly face (Hancock's, I should say, not the murderer's) we were able to get to the bottom of things before the ice creams would have been dispatched for the interval.

In solving this mystery, you'll need to work out the answers to the following questions:

1. **What** was the victim's name?

2. **Who** were the three prime suspects?

3. **Which** suspect was the actual killer?

4. **Why** had they committed the crime?

There's plenty to be getting on with, but make sure you keep an eye on the events happening around you – there's sure to be some useful detail that's worth remembering for later.

Good luck,

Mrs Whitstable

A Dramatic Ending
A Tragedy of Errors

Before I took to my seat and the lights dimmed, I riffled through the programme I had been given. I had been warned by the steward that a printing error had affected some pages, but I took one anyway, assuming it wouldn't be a hindrance. How wrong I was! Whoever had printed the page showing the cast list had actually not printed the names of the actors next to their characters. Honestly.

I politely mentioned this to the steward who told me not to worry; he could easily remember enough information about the list of actors to help me fill in the blanks. I hadn't been worried, per se, though the information came in very handy just a few moments later, when the actor playing Madonna was killed offstage.

Role	Actor
Hercules	
Madonna	
Neris	
Oriole	
Sven	
Gloria	
Agnes	
Vladimir	

To do: work out which actor had been given which part, and which of them was the victim

Notes from a partly-helpful conversation with George Hillock, part-time theatre steward

- Helena played the part of Gloria

- Lindsey was listed immediately after Meera, and neither were at the bottom or top of the list

- Glenda was not the last name on the list

- Roger was listed immediately before Sally

- There were more than two names in between Sally's and Helena's

- William was listed before Max, but not immediately before

- William's name was four names down from Roger's

What was the victim's name?

_____

A Dramatic Ending
A Closer Look at Chaos

Fortunately, the charming Detective Hancock had also fancied an evening of culture, and was in the audience. Upon hearing the screams from the actors backstage, he immediately began to investigate what turned out to be a murder. He ordered the actors back to their individual dressing rooms, demanding that they leave the doors open, presumably to keep an eye on them as much as he could. The audience – who were suddenly witness to something much more dramatic than a work of theatre – were ordered to stay in their seats.

I was dismayed not to be able to leap up and join in the investigating, though I found I was able to contribute to the case from the comfort of my seat. From my seated position, I found I had a very good view towards the rooms off the side of the stage – which doubled up as tea rooms when the stage wasn't in use – each of which had an actor's name on. Through the stage binoculars I had with me, I could see that three of the actors had closed the doors to their dressing rooms. What were they hiding? Needless to say, they became the prime suspects – once I had deciphered who they were.

To do: work out from the binocular view which three actors should be considered the prime suspects

Suspect #1

Suspect #2

Suspect #3

Which three actors were the prime suspects?

_____

A Dramatic Ending
A Tough Act to Follow

I had the names of my three suspects in mind, and having caught the eye of Hancock I shuffled over to give him the news. He seemed rather grateful to have me on side, which is nice – though I suppose he did have a whole audience watching closely as he tried to do his job.

He plucked the three suspect actors from their dressing rooms, and proceeded to interview them. Just before he did so, however, he was stopped by the show's director, who passed us a most intriguing note:

> These three actors are slippery customers: one of them always lies, one of them always tells the truth and the third one... dabbles in both.
> Be careful who you believe.

Whatever training they might have had – or not had – the actors played their parts extremely convincingly. Nevertheless, there was no doubt that the actor who always lied was the one who murdered the poor girl.

To do: work out which of the three suspects – whose names you have already established – is the one who always lies, and is therefore the murderer

Direct quotes taken from Hancock's interviews with each of the three actors:

Suspect 1:
'Oh, alright then, you got me! Put me in handcuffs now. I always lie, I can't help it. I've been lying to everyone for as long as I could talk.'

Suspect 2:
'I'm a very versatile actor – I think it keeps a freshness in my performance – so sometimes I tell the truth.'

Suspect 3:
'I'm an all or nothing sort of person, so I'm not the one who sometimes lies. I try to be consistent with my storytelling – it's the mark of a good actor, you know.'

Which of the three suspects was the murderer?

A Dramatic Ending

The Great Pretender

We had our murderer – but not the motive. The victim was supposedly a close friend of the killer, and they had been known to rehearse together, practising line runs and preparing for auditions. After some questions from Hancock, and some astute observation from me, the truth emerged from amongst the tragedy.

The list of plays suggested for the group's next performance had been released that very day, for consideration by the acting troupe. The killer felt threatened by her friend's on-stage prowess, and decided to remove her from the running once and for all. Of course, the only role they had won was the one of 'cold-blooded killer' – not a credit one wants to one's name.

All five of the suggested plays had been written by William Shakespeare, and each had a title which was one word long. We found evidence of the list inside the killer's dressing room, which had been torn into several pieces. According to the director the list had been sorted alphabetically, and the third play on the list was the one most likely to be chosen.

To do: work out from the fragments which plays had been suggested, then sort them alphabetically to reveal which play was next

Which play did the murderer want a lead role in?

_____

A Dramatic Ending
Case Closed

The curtain was closing on the day's events, and frankly I was glad of it. A young woman had been killed, and the subsequent investigation had been conducted in front of a large audience. Well, I say large: there were more than thirty people on the rows of chairs, so quite a good turnout for the BEADS. Hancock didn't seem too fazed by the crowd, which was just as well, as the murder had quickly become the most dramatic spectacle the village hall had ever witnessed. And that's where they hold the bingo nights.

We had our murderer, and we had uncovered the motive, but there was still so little I could understand about this apparently remorseless killer. When questioned, the murderer said that the actors had spent much of the day discussing the suggested plays. The victim had been rather impassioned about the script which looked most likely to be chosen, and expressed that she had long wished to play the wife of the protagonist. Unfortunately for her, she was hoping for a role also coveted by a senseless murderer.

The killer suggested that the director seemed to favour the victim when choosing leading ladies for his productions, and considered it unfair. By all accounts she had been a splendid actress, and the rest of the cast were naturally horrified at what had occurred behind the red curtains and creaking boards. Privately I wondered whether the director had spotted the killer's serious cold-heartedness and thought that it might come across somewhat unfavourably onstage.

The BEADS had lost two of their most committed actresses: one to her untimely death and the other to a lengthy prison sentence. Naturally the run of the play I had been attempting to watch was cut short, and they also decided not to perform the Shakespeare which had been the root of such tragedy in their group.

The show must go on, however, as it always does. The group still does perform as an ensemble, though they do seem to stick to comedies these days, having seen quite enough of tragedy to last them a lifetime. I, for my part, decided that not even a tub of ice cream might tempt me back to watch another of their productions – the one performance I had seen was quite dramatic enough for me.

With one eye on the case, did you spot these other background scenes? Test your powers of observation by answering the following questions:

1. What was the name of the theatre steward?

2. Who was playing the role of Hercules in the play?

3. What did the dressing rooms double up as, when the stage was not in use?

4. Who was the author of all of the suggested plays?

COLD COMFORT

Another Case Solved by

Mrs Agnes Whitstable

Cold Comfort

When the snow falls in Bishop's End, a pleasing silence falls with it. The roads become quieter and the sound of snowball fights is absorbed into the drift, leaving quiet behind. On those chilly nights, I like to snuggle up by the fire and read a novel – a good mystery novel, of course, will always be my choice. I enjoy the sound of the stillness outside, broken only perhaps by the serene crackling of a fire in a grate, somewhere cosy. It was on one such winter's evening that the following case arose.

I had just settled down in my armchair with a hot cup of peppermint tea and a good book, and closed my eyes for a moment to better appreciate the quiet world around me. No sooner had I done so, however, than there was a blood-curdling scream from the other side of the wall I was sitting right next to. What on earth had happened in the house next-door to mine?

I rushed around to see what was the matter – as fast as one can rush in sheepskin slippers – and was confronted with a scene straight out of a crime novel. The family next door had been having a gathering of sorts, and it seemed to have been an all-day affair. By the looks of things, the guests had been snowed in and decided to have a merry time of it, isolated from the world outside. Many of them seemed to have been members of the family, and you might wonder what on earth had happened to disturb this otherwise idyllic scene.

The owner of the house, my neighbour, was a Mrs Davina Cricket. She lived alone, but always seemed to be having family and friends around for catch-ups and dinner parties. I didn't much mind; she was a good sort of neighbour, and nobody ever seemed to have any bother with her. Or so I thought.

In fact, someone had had so much bother with poor Mrs Cricket that they had killed her on that cold winter's evening, by the cover of dark.

Whoever had done the killing must have thought they had used an untraceable weapon. It didn't take me long, however, to spot that while the offending item would never be found, it was certainly easy to know what it had been: an icicle. The killer had either never picked up a crime novel set in the Alps, or never met me before. Either way, I had all the evidence I needed to unpick the mystery of my poor neighbour's fate.

With the roads impassable, and the phone lines out of use, it was up to me alone to determine which of the party guests had done the unspeakable deed. The matter was close to home – quite literally – so it was rather important to me that I conduct the investigation with the utmost care. On the following pages you'll find the snippets of evidence I came across, and which I later used to bring the cold-blooded killer to justice. *Very* cold-blooded, given the weather.

To solve the mystery, you'll need to uncover the answers to the following questions:

1. **How** many opportunities were there for the killer to strike?

2. **Who** are the two main suspects?

3. **What** is the killer's name?

4. **What** was the killer's motive?

As ever, you'll do well to keep an eye out for anything else you spot as you solve your way through the mystery. Expect the unexpected – that's what I always say!

   Good luck,

   Mrs Whitstable

Cold Comfort
Straight Out of the Blocks

The victim's house had an old-style outhouse in the grounds for storing ice. Despite the cold weather, the gathering of the family had clearly required some cold refreshment inside, and several trips to the ice house had been made that day. In fact, the victim was attacked on one of those very journeys. Chilling stuff.

Inside the ice house was a large block of ice which had been split into several much smaller cubes, for ease of removal. The large arrangement had once been a 4×4×4 stack of these cubes, though several had been taken since then. On the morning before the murder, there were exactly 56 cubes in the block.

Each time the victim travelled back and forth between the house and the ice house that day, they took exactly one of these smaller cubes away with them. No one else had removed any ice on that day, and the killer had clearly planned to intercept them on one of these journeys. But how many opportunities had they had to do so? I've included a photograph opposite of the ice block, taken just after the killing.

To do: work out how many ice blocks had been removed on the day of the murder, and therefore how many opportunities there were for the victim to be intercepted

How many opportunities were there for the victim to be intercepted?

_____

Cold Comfort
Something's Afoot

There had also been sleet and rain on the day of the murder, and several muddy footprints appeared across the house. Clearly each of the printmakers had been outside that day and could be considered a suspect. A right shoe was taken from each of the suspects which matched the right shoe of each set of prints.

Before examining the shoes, however, I noticed something rather offbeat about the sets of prints themselves. It looked to me like two people had put their shoes on in a hurry – and they became my prime suspects.

Pictured below are the prints taken from each right shoe, and opposite is the photograph of the muddy footprints in the hallway. Let's just say I was pleased to have been there to just clear up the mystery of the murder, and not the mire on the floor.

To do: spot two sets of unusual footprints and use them to determine the two prime suspects. Call the leftmost of those below 'suspect A', and the other 'suspect B'

Archie Plum	Glen Walker	Clive Young	Suzy Feathers	Maeve Brown

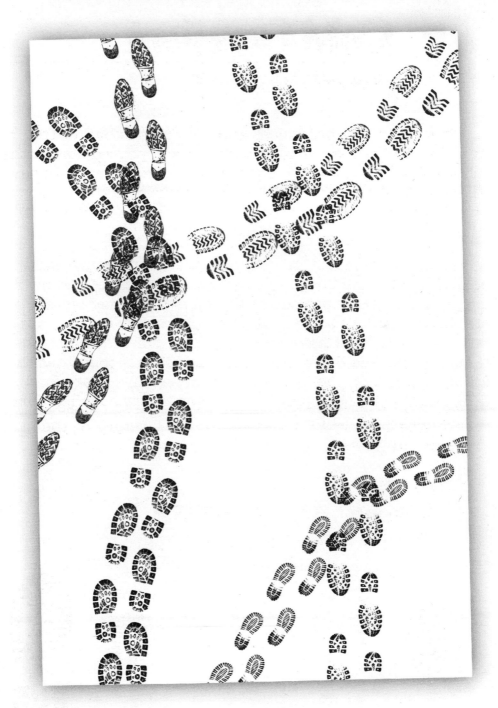

Who are the two prime suspects?

_____

Cold Comfort

When Hell Freezes Over

I like people who are prompt, and cannot bear lateness. Whoever killed poor Davina Cricket clearly had an excellent sense of timing, though I realize that their personal virtues are not worth unpacking here. Nonetheless, it was clear that the murderer had waited for the opportune moment to commit their crime.

The murder had occurred when the temperature was below freezing outside, i.e. less than 0°C. Both of the prime suspects had some periods of the day when they were accounted for, and some when they were not. One of those latter periods must have overlapped with a time when the temperature was below freezing – and it was then that the killer had struck. I've included a temperature chart for the afternoon's weather opposite, and my record of when each of the suspects had been vouched for below.

Suspect A

Accounted for:

12.30pm – 2.45pm

3.50pm – 5.30 pm

7.15pm – 8.45pm

Suspect B

Accounted for:

12.05pm – 1.45pm

3pm – 5.10pm

5.50pm – 7.15pm

To do: work out from the temperature chart when the outside temperature was below 0°C at the same time that a suspect was unaccounted for

READINGS TAKEN FROM THE OUTDOOR THERMOMETER

Time	Reading
Midday	5°C
1pm	dropped by 2°C
2pm	rose by 3°C
3pm	dropped by 4°C
4pm	dropped by 3°C
5pm	rose by 2°C
6pm	dropped by 3°C
7pm	rose by 2°C
8pm	rose by 5°C

Which of the two suspects committed the crime, and when?

_____

Cold Comfort

The Pyramid Scheme

Another killer caught, another suspect sniffed out...
another senseless loss of life. I confronted the killer with
my suspicions, and they crumbled under the accusations.
Once again, I had been left without a motive. What had
Davina Cricket done to deserve such misfortune? There is
no justification for the crime, though the killer did talk.

Davina had planned to change her will and cut all
family members out of their inheritance. Instead, she
wanted to invest in a pyramid scheme, where more and
more money would be taken from her over time – though
with absolutely no chance of return, according to her
killer. They decided to put a stop to things before the will
was changed and the family fortune was lost.

There would initially be five small payments, then four,
then three and so on until one final 'investment'. Each
payment was set out in a scheme so that each individual
payment was the sum total of the two payments directly
'below' it. Five example amounts, from three different
levels, had already been suggested, and Davina had agreed
to complete the pyramid, giving more and more money at
each level.

The bottom line of the scheme opposite shows two of
the first five example payments. I could see that, when all
of the investments had been made, Davina stood to lose an
awful lot of money.

To do: *complete the number pyramid to reveal how much the victim planned to invest at each stage, and then add all the payments to reveal the total which would be lost*

Number pyramid:

- Top: 4230
- Row 2: 2180, 2050
- Row 3: 1050, 1130, 920
- Row 4: 430, 620, 510, 410
- Bottom: 150, 280, 340, 170, 240

How much money did the victim stand to lose?

_____

Cold Comfort

Case Closed

So there we had it. Money had driven a family member to despair, and they had decided to put a stop to things once and for all. The rest of the guests at the party – not that it felt much like a party when I left – did not share in the killer's feelings at all. Instead, they were horrified that someone might turn on a member of their own family, and especially one who had welcomed them all with such warm hospitality.

The killer protested that they had the interest of the surviving family members at heart, but the protest naturally fell on deaf and grieving ears. There was some remonstration from some of the family elders, but the chief emotion seemed to be one of quiet shock. Silence had returned to Bishop's End, but not of the kind I find enjoyable.

It was a heartbreaking scene, not least because the table had been set for supper with a most delightful cheeseboard that they were probably not going to touch now. But I digress.

By the time I had uncovered the identity of the killer, the telephone lines had been reconnected, and the police called. The criminal was apprehended after the constables on duty were satisfied that my investigation had handed them the correct suspect. Interestingly, none of them had ever heard of an icicle featuring so prominently in a murder case – perhaps it really is just the stuff of mystery novels.

When Davina Cricket's house had fallen silent once more, with the guests variously mourning and attempting to depart, in spite of the snow, I returned to my own house, my slippers quite soaked through. It had been a distressing evening for all those involved, though there was one small sting left in the tail of the day: my hot beverage was now well below the optimum drinking temperature.

Time to put the kettle on.

Did you freeze under the pressure, or did you manage to keep your cool? Test your powers of observation by answering the following questions:

1. What had I been about to drink before I heard the commotion next door?

2. How many smaller cubes had originally been in the stack in the ice house, when the large block was first installed?

3. Which person had the smallest shoes of all the footprints shown?

4. How many individual payments would the victim have made if she completed her pyramid scheme?

THE DIAMOND AND THE ROUGH

Another Case Solved by

Mrs Agnes Whitstable

The Diamond and the Rough

Bishop's End is something between a small town and a large village, with plenty of shops and businesses for anything one might need. There are the usual staples (butcher, baker, although not a candlestick maker) and the occasional more specialist establishment. There was once, for example, a small shop owned by a man who exclusively repaired oboes and clarinets. He didn't sell new ones and nor did he repair other woodwind instruments: that was quite out of his remit. Needless to say, the business didn't have too many customers to trouble it.

One of Bishop's End's many other establishments is that of a watchmaker and jewel specialist known as Mr Hickory. I laughed when I first heard the name, but apparently it comes from the pecan-like nut and not the nursery rhyme about mice and clocks. His shop is a small one, but for years the residents of Bishop's End have taken their broken clocks, rings and necklaces to him in the hope of restoration, as well as seeking out new and shiny items.

One day, several years ago now, I had planned to take a necklace of pearls to Mr Hickory so that he might restring them for me. The knotted cord that held them together was beginning to fray in places, and I couldn't bear the thought of chasing after the tiny jewels if the necklace ever gave up the ghost on me at an unexpected moment. When I entered the shop, however, I realized that my pearls were not the only thing that might unravel that day.

The shop – usually sparklingly clean – was in complete disarray, with broken cabinets, jewels on the floor and, most significantly, a very shaken Mr Hickory behind the counter. His shop had just fallen victim to an attempted robbery, though the perpetrator was now gone. I must have an excellent nose for trouble: apparently the thief had fled just a few moments before I arrived, and Mr Hickory hadn't even had time to summon the authorities.

When I asked what had been taken from the shop, fearing that he might have lost large quantities of fine watches and jewels, Mr Hickory faltered. There was a moment, he said, when the thief seemed to have had a change of heart, and emptied his pockets of the loot he had been about to make off with. Of course, rings and brooches are small items, so he may have made off with a few of those whether wittingly or not.

Needless to say, I was intrigued. A distracted thief who apparently had a crisis of confidence – or perhaps a crisis of conscience – was just the sort of criminal I wanted to find on that otherwise uneventful Wednesday. I had been planning to purchase a pair of kippers for tomorrow's breakfast after I dropped off the pearls, but that task immediately slipped to the bottom of my to-do list. I had a much more slippery customer that I wanted to catch before then.

To solve the mystery, you'll need to find out the answers to the following questions:

1. **What** time did the robbery take place?

2. **How** did the thief manage to free themselves?

3. **Why** had the thief turned and run?

4. **Who** was the thief?

Aside from these pressing issues, keep your eye out for other details in the background. What may seem ordinary at first may turn out to be very important information later on!

Good luck,

Mrs Whitstable

The Diamond and the Rough

A Really Smashing Time

Mr Hickory had, on the morning of the robbery, been brought a watch to repair, which was waiting on the counter for his full attention. During the fracas, however, the watch face had been smashed, and the watch stopped. Initially, I thought this a happy accident since it would allow me to determine the exact time of the attack, and perhaps narrow down a few suspects.

The reason the watch had been brought in, however, was because it was faulty – and therefore it hadn't been showing the correct time. When I peered closely, I could see that the watch had been smashed when it showed the time as 1.32pm, though this was, alas, much earlier than the real time of the attack. Time to rethink, so to speak.

Luckily, Mr Hickory was an efficient business owner, and kept excellent records of his customers' needs. Here is the receipt he created for the customer when the watch was brought in, which allowed me to solve the problem in a very timely fashion – if you'll pardon the pun.

To do: work out when the robbery took place from the time on the slow watch

MR HICKORY'S
WATCHES AND DIAMONDS

FINE JEWELS AND TICKING CLOCKS

Order Received

Customer Name: Richard Wales

Item brought in: Watch (wind-up)

Problem: Watch running slowly. Loses six (6) minutes for every hour

Time showing on watch when brought in: 9.02

Actual time watch brought in: 10am

Please keep this for your records

At exactly what time did the attack take place?

_____

The Diamond and the Rough

Keep the Cogs Turning

The thief should have been stopped by a secure barrier at the door, controlled by a turning handle next to Mr Hickory's desk. The watchmaker had never had to use the security gate prior to the day of the attack, although I suppose there's a first time for everything.

The turning handle was positioned next to the leftmost cog marked '1' on the photograph opposite, and turning the handle so that the cog turns anti-clockwise closes the security gate. Mr Hickory did indeed successfully use it to bring the gate down, but unfortunately only after the perpetrator was within the store – and I suppose at that moment he realized he was now sealed into his own shop with a man who had attempted to steal from him. A wasp in a jar springs to mind.

Fortunately, the thief took one look at the mechanism and understood how to reverse the motion of the security gate. The final cog in the mechanism – marked '2' in the photograph – was closest to the thief, and he simply turned the cog to open the gate and escape. But which way did he turn it?

To do: work out which way the cog marked '2' must be turned to open the gate

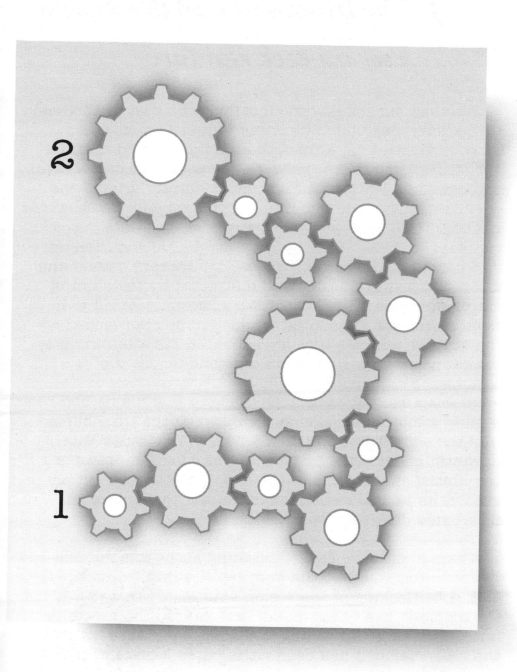

Which way should cog '2' turn to open the gate?

_____

The Diamond and the Rough

Looking Back and Forth

And now we come to the most curious part of this tale. Mr Hickory was understandably quite relieved to be no longer trapped with a thief, though it did now mean the robber had free rein to ransack the shop and its valuable contents, and leave. The thief paced quickly around the premises, shoving jewels into his pockets and watches into his bag.

I personally have always liked Mr Hickory's shop and often find myself dazzled and distracted by the shining wares on display. The same fate, however, seemed to have befallen the would-be larcener; just as he approached the counter with Mr Hickory behind it, his attention was caught by a large, square-cut diamond on the top.

It was a beauty, to be sure. Hickory told me he had been setting it into an engagement ring when the thief burst into the shop. When the thief saw this particular jewel, however, he let out a gasp of horror, hurriedly returned the almost-stolen items to the shop's owner and left as quickly as he had come. It was not the way robberies usually go, that's for sure.

There must have been something about this specific diamond that shocked the man into leaving without his loot. After looking at the scene, I suggested that it was not the diamond itself that might have caused the reaction, but the detail it was hiding. My suspicions were confirmed: the huge diamond had been sitting atop a piece of paper marked with the name of the girl it was intended for, although the cut of the gem had reflected and obscured parts of her name. Whoever she was, the name and ring together must have meant something to the thief.

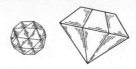

To do: decipher the person's name from the view obscured by the diamond

Who was the ring intended for?

_____

The Diamond and the Rough

A Thief of Love

I surmised that the thief was in love with someone whose name matched the one he had read, and whose would-be engagement ring he had spotted on the jeweller's desk. But where was the thief now? Even without having stolen anything, he still needed to be tracked down.

As it happened, I knew someone of the very name I had seen under the diamond: the daughter of Mr and Mrs Tiverton, who run the greengrocers. I popped over to see if she was acting suspiciously, but she turned out instead to be a mine of information. She told me she had been going steady with a boy named Timothy Winters, who I learned from Mr Hickory was the man who had ordered the engagement ring. I kept quiet about the ring, but asked if she had been receiving unusual attention from anyone else lately.

She told me that, in fact, she had received some very strange missives from a secret admirer who she knew to have been a delivery boy for her parents at some stage or other. It seems that he was slowly revealing his identity to her, albeit cryptically with a series of word-based clues.

I compared the letters sent by the strange courier against the list of names given to me by her parents and, at long last, unpicked the unusual tale.

To do: work out from the notes and the potential names which boy is likely to be the thief

My first and last names both begin with letters in the first half of the alphabet

My first and last names have a different number of letters

My surname has more letters than my first name

My surname doesn't end in 'N'

List of boys who had worked for the Tivertons at one time or another:

Alexander Chilton

Chris Harrison

Henry Fuller

James Green

Tom Phillips

Wallis Herman

Which of the boys is the would-be thief?

_____

The Diamond and the Rough

Case Closed

I made my way back to Mr Hickory's shop with the news that I had found the person responsible, and he did seem rather pleased to have got to the bottom of it. He had more or less put the shop back in order when I arrived, and was pleased to confirm that all valuable items were accounted for. I put in a call to Hancock and told him of my afternoon's activities – he promised to call around at the young offender's home and straighten things out properly.

Mr Hickory was so grateful for my help that he offered to repair the pearls I had brought in free of charge: an unexpected boon for the day. It was a fair exchange for an afternoon's investigations and the lost opportunity for a breakfast kipper for the next day.

He did not stop there, however. I suspect he was so flushed with relief that nothing of great value had been stolen that he went above and beyond with a display of gratitude for me. After rummaging around in his storeroom for a minute or so, he produced a small package wrapped in cloth. Most curious.

Years ago, someone had brought in an antique item that they wished to be repaired. It had a handle set with pearls, some of which were damaged and some of which had come off altogether. Mr Hickory dutifully repaired the artefact with the care and precision he is known for, but the customer never came back to collect it. He had called the number on the receipt, but the line went nowhere: it had been disconnected.

In the years that passed between those days and the afternoon of the robbery, Mr Hickory kept the item carefully stored away, in case it ever came in handy – or in case he found the right person to bestow it upon. Apparently that day had now come, and he offered it to me, handing it over carefully in its wrappings so that I might admire it for myself. I usually try not to accept material gifts in exchange for my investigations, but in this case I could not resist.

What was the antique item? A small, delightfully embellished magnifying glass, just right for someone with an eye for detail and a penchant for solving mysteries.

Were you distracted by the sparkling jewels, or did you keep your eye on the prize? Test your powers of observation by answering the following questions:

1. Which two instruments could once be repaired in a very specific shop in Bishop's End?

2. What was the name of the watch owner, whose watch was running slow?

3. Which couple ran the greengrocers?

4. How many names were on the list of delivery boys?

THE PLOT THICKENS

Another Case Solved by

Mrs Agnes Whitstable

The Plot Thickens

Nobody – not even, say, an elderly investigator who makes a splendid crumble – wants to find out that there's been a murder close to home. It's an unsettling thing to experience at any distance, but Bishop's End seems to have had more than its fair share of killings over the years. Perhaps there's something in the water.

If you ever venture into Bishop's End – and don't let the murders put you off – you will notice that to the south of the village is a quiet garden which benefits from several hours of sunshine. There are benches on which one might take advantage of said weather, and plentiful flowers and herbs border the edges, full of bees and colour. These days it is considered a charming and peaceful spot. Several years ago, however, it was the site of a rather grisly murder.

Back then, the green space was a set of allotments, run by a community of keen gardeners. Each gardener had their own little patch, and as a group had named themselves the Bishop's End Allotment Network (or BEAN, for short). The BEANers seemed to be a happy lot, growing actual beans to their heart's content alongside other roots and shoots of all varieties. The group seemingly rubbed along well enough, with the occasional dispute about whose watering can was whose. So far, so idyllic.

One day, however, one of the gardeners was discovered in his allotment, quite dead. The victim was a man named Martin, who had had a long profession as a cobbler and was still known to reheel the occasional distressed winter boot, if asked nicely. He had

turned his attention to his allotment after retiring, and clearly had a natural talent for it. His vegetables always looked splendid in the autumn harvests, and he regularly won prizes for his green-fingered success. Alas, all this nature and nurture would eventually be the death of him.

I leapt into investigating the case with Detective Hancock, who had been assigned to it. He clearly (and accurately) surmised that I was above suspicion and allowed me to assist him; a wise move, given my local knowledge. My main source of information was Emma Waterman, allotment supervisor and the

de facto leader of the BEAN. She was quite upset at the discovery of Martin's murder, especially as there had been some tension among the gardeners recently. There were, she said, at least two serious disputes going on among the BEANers when Martin was killed. I decided it would be best to start with these, as I had a free afternoon and a penchant for solving mysterious crimes.

If only I knew then what I know now. Of all of the cases I have looked into, I think none have surprised me quite as much as this did. Here, then, are my case notes on the matter. There are eight pieces of evidence, a baffling twist in the tale and a senseless murder to solve. What's not to like?

To solve the mystery, you'll need to establish the answers to the following questions:

1. **What** had the deceased been planning?

2. **How** were they murdered?

3. **What** plant had played a role?

4. **Who** had seen Martin on the day of his death?

5. **What** were the murderer's initials?

As ever, keep your eyes peeled for anything that looks out of place while you unravel the mystery. Observation saves lives! Although, alas, not Martin's.

Good luck,

Mrs Whitstable

The Plot Thickens
Allotted Areas

The source of the first dispute was simple enough. An elderly gardener had wanted to give up their plot after suffering a spell of backache when trying to dig up some particularly well-rooted carrots. The gardener – a most appropriately named Mr Green – had used twine to split his allotment into several distinct rectangular areas to monitor crop rotation, create effective irrigation systems and keep an eye on the most hated of foes: slugs.

The Bishop's End Allotment Network had decided to split up Mr Green's now-unused plot between themselves, and each member would take over a small section. Unfortunately, they simply could not agree on how many possible different sizes of sections Mr Green had marked out with his twine, if combining them was allowed, and spent several hours debating the total number of possible rectangular areas. According to Emma Waterman, the quibbles involved the following numbers:

- Suzanna thought there were at least 50 regions
- Martin thought there were 45 to 50 regions
- Micah thought there were from 40 to 45 regions
- Hans thought there were between 30 and 40 regions
- Petros thought there were no more than 30 regions

Emma thought that at least two of the members might have been correct, but I spotted only one. I personally thought they all seemed to have lost the plot.

To do: count the total number of distinct rectangular areas that can be formed by the string in the allotment, including the outer perimeter

How many rectangular areas are visible?
Who was correct in their calculations?

_____

The Plot Thickens
Leeked Information

On the day of Martin's death, the allotments had been abuzz with a planting spree. It was a fine autumn day, with a cool breeze passing through the almost-ready vegetables, and rays of sunshine peeping through gaps in the cloud. The place was full of life, and ripe legumes – although death, too, but nobody knew that yet, except perhaps the murderer.

Several members of the Bishop's End Allotment Network had ventured out to plant hardy vegetables which would survive the winter. Martin was one of them, and I wanted to know who he had crossed paths with. I spoke to the omniscient Emma, who as usual had kept her eyes on the comings and goings of the day. Some might call her nosy, but a nosy person is a useful sort to have around when a crime has been committed.

It seemed that none of the gardeners had really spoken to one another during the course of the day, and had each appeared at different times. Nonetheless, I wanted to speak to whomever had been gardening immediately before and immediately after Martin had planted his winter stock.

Emma gave me the following information:

- Geraldine was seen planting leeks before Suzanna planted cabbage, but not immediately before

- Hans planted his vegetables immediately after the kale was planted

- Martin was not the last person to be seen out planting

- Micah was seen planting vegetables immediately after Hans planted his own

- Petros was the second person seen planting, but he did not plant kale

- The cabbage was planted before the turnips, but not immediately before

- The last vegetable to be planted was chard

- The turnips were planted after the garlic, but not immediately after

To do: work out who planted which vegetables and in what order, and identify the two gardeners spotted either side of Martin's planting session

	Person	**Vegetable**
1.		
2.		
3.		
4.		
5.		
6.		

Who were the two people to speak to?

_____

The Plot Thickens

What's Your Poison?

I questioned the two relevant gardeners, and they both told me that they had seen Martin stumbling around in his allotment, squinting at his plant labels in confusion. As I pondered the meaning of it, a message from Detective Hancock arrived, saying that while a weapon had certainly been used to kill Martin, there was also strong evidence that he had been poisoned first. A plot twist, if you will.

In Martin's allotment, the plants indicated by the two other gardeners contained, to my great surprise, several leaves and flowers which I knew to be highly toxic. In fact, one of them had clearly been recently disturbed, with some sprigs freshly pruned. I suspected that this was the plant that had poisoned Martin – but how might such a keen horticulturist fall victim to his own garden?

Martin was fastidiously organized: the ten poisonous plants had been arranged in a neat row, in alphabetical order of the plant's name, reading from left to right along the line. The plant fifth from the left was the one which had been disturbed, although the name labels had somehow been removed from their places and muddied to obscure them. I set about working out which was what.

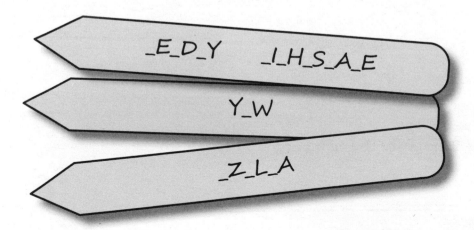

To do: complete each of the names of these dangerous plants, one letter per gap, then sort into alphabetical order to establish which one was used to poison Martin

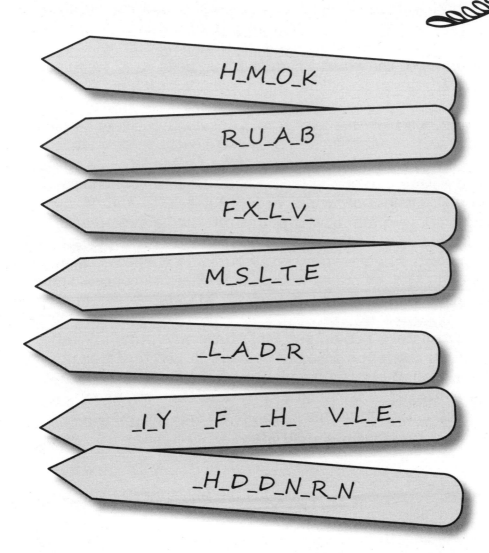

H_M_O_K

R_U_A_B

F_X_L_V_

M_S_L_T_E

_L_A_D_R

_I_Y _F _H_ V_L_E_

_H_D_D_N_R_N

Which plant had been used to poison Martin?

_____

The Plot Thickens
Breaking New Ground

I had a strong suspicion that Martin hadn't just become a little peckish and snacked on one of his own poisonous plants. I sent a message back to Detective Hancock with the name of the plant I deduced had been used to poison poor Martin, and decided to investigate further.

Martin's plot was also host to several entirely edible fruits and vegetables, all arranged neatly in geometric beds. Perhaps he had been inspired by Mr Green's twine, since within one of the larger beds he had constructed a complex system of twine-bordered areas, though in a way which allowed him to travel around his beloved plants easily enough. I noticed, however, that several pieces of the twine had been recently cut, and suspected that someone had sabotaged the neat borders to conceal their tracks when choosing a poison for Martin.

Fortunately, I could see that there was only one way in which the twine could have been linked together in the first place, in the one continuous loop that Martin had arranged. I sketched a copy and then set about reconstructing it, so that I could retrace the steps of whoever had poisoned Martin.

To do: recreate the twine loop so it visits every circular post just once, without ever crossing over itself. Only horizontal and vertical lines of twine between posts are allowed. Some sections of twine are already in place.

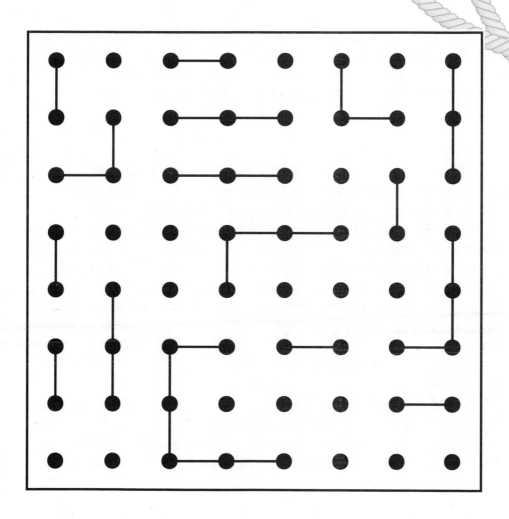

Can you recreate the victim's neat borders in order to trace the movements of whoever poisoned him?

The Plot Thickens

May Contain Traces of Murder

Some people are blessed with green thumbs and a gift for bringing life to a garden. I personally cannot keep a house plant alive, but I have been gifted with sharp observation skills and marvellous eyesight. Excellent for spotting dropped stitches in a jumper, lumps in gravy or, more appropriately for this case, evidence of a murder.

Near to the location where Martin was found fatally wounded were some spots of compost in an arrangement that caught my eye. Compost in a vegetable garden is, of course, not that unusual, but there was something that didn't seem quite right with the scene in front of me. This compost was new, and rather fresh-looking. It certainly didn't match any of the compost in Martin's beds, but the pattern it made on the ground looked like someone had set down a gardening tool right next to the spot where Martin was killed. But was it a gardening tool, or was it a murder weapon? Or indeed, was it both?

Feeling sure this was an outline of the murder weapon I sought, I made a rough sketch of the compost dots – shown opposite – and set about trying to determine the type of object we were looking for. Lumpy gravy this was not!

To do: join the dots in order of increasing number until the outline of a murder weapon is revealed

13 12
14
7 8 1
15
6
16 5 4
17 47
46

11
10
2
3 9
49
48

18
45

19
44

22
27 21 20
23 26 28 31 43
32 35 42
37 41
36
40

24
25
29
30
33 34
38 39

What was the murder weapon?

_____

The Plot Thickens

A Calculated Error

With my discovery of the likely murder weapon, the source of the second dispute came to light. Emma Waterman appeared just as I was examining the spots of new compost, and sighed deeply. Martin had thought an unused section of the Bishop's End allotments could be made into a community garden for residents, with kitchen herbs for anyone who might wander by and fancy a sprig of rosemary or thyme to accompany their supper. Yum.

Emma had been in favour of the idea, she said, but there was much grumbling over the cost of compost. The other gardeners didn't want to fork out for the community project – so to speak – but Martin had drawn up the plans and ordered the compost anyway. Alas, it seems, this was the death of him.

Martin's half-drawn plans for the bed are shown opposite, with all the necessary information for calculating the amount of compost needed to cover all three areas. Scribbled on the back of the plan were the following notes in the dead man's handwriting:

Largest of the three areas
is a perfect square

All measurements an
exact number of metres

Cost of compost = £1 / m²

Total compost cost = ???

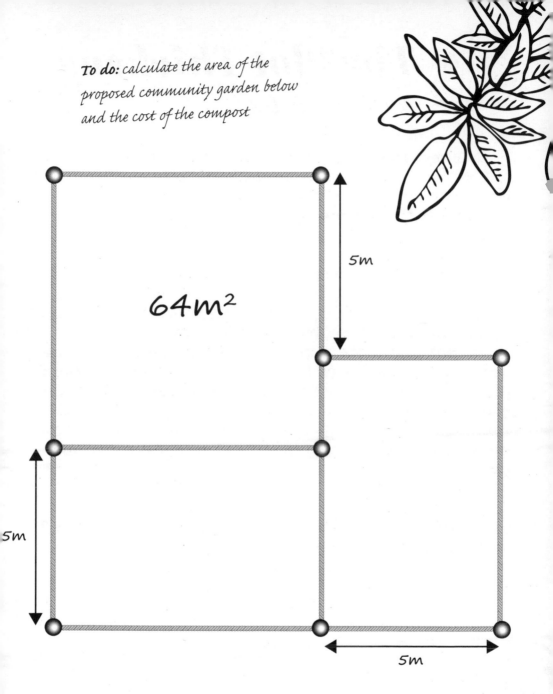

64m²

5m

5m

5m

How much had Martin claimed the new compost would cost the gardeners?

_____

The Plot Thickens

Digging the Dirt

Detective Hancock appeared just as I made my way over to the pile of fresh compost, which had been delivered just before the murder and unceremoniously dumped near the entrance to the Bishop's End allotments. Hancock and I shared the same suspicions over the murder weapon, as well as the poison given to Martin. The killer and motive, however, were still completely unknown.

Someone had spread out the compost so that it covered a roughly square area, but my beady eyes spotted something else in the mire: a flash of orange. Martin had been growing pumpkins for years, and frequently entered them into the Bishop's End vegetable competition, usually winning first prize. Someone had clearly had enough of his winning streak, having cut his magnificent pumpkins from the vine and buried them in the soft compost meant for the community garden.

Hancock was ready to dive into the pile – figuratively, I hoped – but with a bit of judicious probing with a stick I found a way to calculate the hidden contents before digging in, and made the following notes:

- Pumpkins are only located in the numberless squares in this grid.

- Numbers show how many pumpkins are in touching squares – including diagonally touching squares.

- No more than one pumpkin can be found in any square.

To do: work out where the prize pumpkins are buried in the compost pile, and how many there are in total

1	3		3	1
				3
		3		
	2		3	
1		1	1	1

How many of Martin's pumpkins had been buried?

The Plot Thickens

The Gloves Are Off

One never knows what the autumn harvest will bring – it is one of mother nature's great mysteries. As Hancock and I uncovered pumpkin after pumpkin in the compost, the allotment offered up its most revealing bounty yet: the murder weapon, and a bloodied gardening glove.

I established that the gardeners had ordered some of their equipment in bulk, including, in particular, their gloves. As such, all of the pairs looked very similar, so each gardener had sewn their initials onto their left-hand glove. Even without this, however, each individual pair was in fact unique, so the gardeners never had trouble identifying their own pair. Hancock pointed out that the glove we had found was for a right hand, and since it was surely the murderer's then we should be able to find a matching left glove with their initials handily stitched on.

Hancock and I recovered all of the pictured gloves from the gardeners. There are seven complete pairs, and one loner – whose bloodied counterpart had been worn by Martin's murderer.

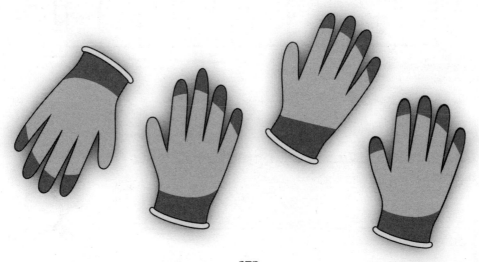

To do: work out which left glove does not have a matching right glove, and reveal the murderer's initials

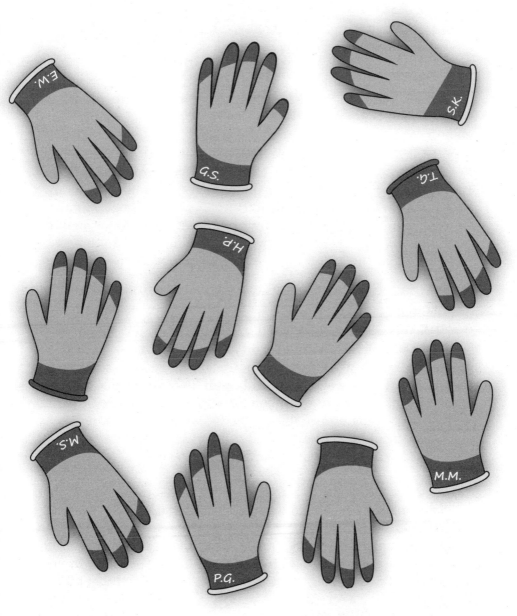

Whose initials were on the glove worn by Martin's murderer?

_____

The Plot Thickens

Case Closed

It's not often that I am left speechless, but I must say that identifying the owner of the bloodied glove was one of those extremely rare moments. Martin's killer was someone that I not only knew personally, but had supposedly helped me in the investigation of the murder. Hancock took a little longer than I to put the pieces together, but eventually the penny dropped. He'd had a long day, after all. It was about to get a lot, lot longer.

We set out across the allotments to discover that the Bishop's End Allotment Network had called an emergency meeting in one of the sheds, and our killer was amongst them. Of course I hoped that Hancock would arrest the perpetrator without the need for an ugly scene, but what unfolded next was more baffling than anything I could have imagined. And I've seen a few strange things in my time.

Hancock confronted the owner of the bloodied glove, announcing his intention to arrest them on suspicion of murder. But the other BEAN members didn't seem at all surprised, and a few members even nodded dolefully, as though in affirmation. There was a mumble of 'fair enough' from one of the gardeners, and some sheepish glances between them. Although there was a gloomy mood in the shed, as one might expect on the occasion of a murder, there was also something unreadable on the faces of these seemingly wholesome gardeners. They looked quite miserable, but not as *horrified* as I expected. What on earth was going on?

The owner of the bloody glove stepped forward and confirmed that, yes, they had been the one to wield the weapon that killed Martin. The deceased man, it seems, was a victim of ambition: the killer had seen Martin's plans to expand the BEAN with a community garden, and wanted to stop the project from going ahead. There was fervent opposition to his schemes, and the killer was concerned that the BEAN might have a schism on its hands. What if Martin wanted to take over as head of the BEAN? What if he wanted to turn the entire plot into a garden for the community? The proverbial pitchforks of protest were out well before the actual fork of death.

But there were more surprises in store. The two gardeners to whom I had spoken earlier in the investigation – the two who had seen Martin gardening on the day of his death – didn't seem surprised to hear that Martin had also been poisoned. To be fair they had both mentioned to me that the victim was acting irrationally, apparently confused by his own poisonous plants, so perhaps the two gardeners had not actually lied to me – but they had certainly omitted an important truth: that they had been the two to poison Martin.

Apparently unhappy with the cultivation of toxic plants in an area where they wished to grow food for their families, the two gardeners decided to give Martin a taste of his own medicine. They confirmed that I had correctly identified the offending plant, and that they had tricked him into ingesting some leaves. They had hoped only to make him a little unwell, so had continued to garden alongside him – just in case something truly terrible befell him.

So murder was not on these two gardeners' agenda, and it was confirmed that Martin hadn't died from the poison, although the experience would have been really quite unpleasant. They hung their heads in shame, and rightly so. I presumed that they felt doubly disgraced, given Martin's untimely demise later that same day, but there was still yet more scandal to uncover from these hellish horticulturists.

The mystery of the buried pumpkins remained. Who had snipped them from the vines, carried them over to the compost pile and buried them in the heap, removing his chances of a competition win? The prized fruits were, frankly, enormous, and the task must have been a significant undertaking for an elderly gardener (and they were certainly all elderly), especially since presumably undertaken during the cover of darkness. However crazed by regular defeat, this suggested to me that this could surely not all be the work of one person. And then as I looked at the gardeners, huddled in the BEAN headquarters, I suddenly realized: there was not one perpetrator here, but many.

And so the truth emerged. Sick of Martin's string of wins at the vegetable competition, the BEAN members had decided to take matters into their own hands – or, rather, gloves. After the poisoning – which I realized had in fact taken place yesterday – they had returned at night to bury his beloved pumpkins, but had unfortunately encountered a problem in the form of Martin himself, who had come to check for nocturnal slugs. He had confronted the group by the light of the moon, the argument had escalated and Martin had been killed. The murderer was the one whose initials we knew, but the entire group was guilty of involvement in his death.

But here, in the hut, they had just found a final sting – and the reason behind the murderous group's gloomy faces. Well, even gloomier than you might suppose a group of murderous gardeners to be. When looking for a place to hide the bloodied glove, the murderer had stumbled across a note written by Martin just before his death. The victim was clearly aware of the group's discontent with his plans, especially from a financial standpoint, and had scribbled the following onto a piece of paper:

Happy to pay for community compost with any future winnings from the vegetable competition – will discuss at next BEAN meeting

The BEAN never did have another meeting, with the group disbanding naturally as several of its key members began to serve prison sentences. The allotments which had brought so much happiness to Martin were razed to the ground, but with good reason: those residents of Bishop's End who hadn't been involved in the murder decided that the plot should become the community garden that Martin had hoped to create just a tiny fragment of.

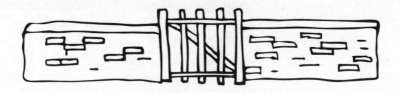

I often stop here and think of poor Martin, and what he might have made of the garden we built in his honour. I do hope it does him some credit. And, while I think of it, I shall take a sprig of thyme home to have with my supper tonight.

Once you've recovered from the shock of it all, cast your mind back and see if you can remember these details from the case:

1. Which of the gardeners was planting leeks on the day of Martin's murder?

2. How many toxic plants had Martin been growing in his allotment?

3. Which gardener had left their allotment to be divided among the rest of the gardeners?

4. What is the name of the society to which all of the gardeners belonged?

DETECTIVE SKILLS

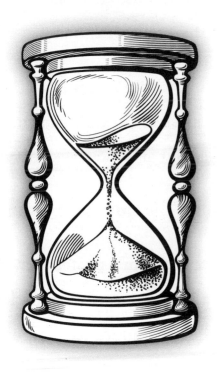

Detective Skills

TICKET TO DIE

1. Which town had I travelled to when I encountered the murder scene?

2. What object had I intended to purchase?

3. What was the name of the police officer at the station?

4. What was the victim's name?

5. How many postcards were sent to the victim?

6. Which bag number at lost property contained a bow tie?

7. What time did the train for Lopton Head leave the station?

8. What was the victim's profession?

9. What was the murderer's occupation?

10. What was I three hours late for, after solving the murder?

Detective Skills

A BUMP IN THE ROAD

1. What nickname did I give my car?

2. How much was a replacement key for the victim's car?

3. What was the name of the woman who owned the stolen car?

4. What was her profession?

5. What were the victim and I discussing when Snipping arrived with the steering wheel?

Detective Skills

THE FORCED HAND

1. What was the name of the pub in which the attack took place?

2. On what day is a steak and kidney pie served there in the evening?

3. Where had I been sitting when the attack took place?

4. What is the barmaid's name?

5. How many times was the napkin folded before there were pieces cut away?

Detective Skills

A WHOLE NEW BALL GAME

1. How many sports clubs used the pavilion as their headquarters?

2. How many matches did the players play away each month?

3. What score did the winning team play to in each game?

4. What local publication did I have a copy of during the investigation?

5. Against which team were the Bishop's End players reported to have lost, in the magazine?

Detective Skills

PAINTED INTO A CORNER

1. What is the name of the home Oscar lived in?

2. How had the thief got into the house?

3. In which country did Oscar's aunt and cousin live?

4. How many staircases were there in total in Oscar's house?

5. Which family member revealed the identity of the thief to Oscar?

Detective Skills

THE WRITING ON THE WALL

1. Which 'offensive' item was uncovered during the search when entering the library?

2. What was the name of the postman's wife?

3. Where was I sitting for the event in the library?

4. How many of Winkleman's books can you name from the stack set aside for signing? There were nine in total.

5. How many sections of the library were there, according to the guide?

6. How many doors were indicated with letters on the library floorplan?

7. What was the person cycling in a green jumper carrying with them?

8. How long could a book be borrowed for at the library?

9. What was the name of Marjorie Winkleman's last novel?

10. Where did I have to travel to finally get my hands on a copy of it?

Detective Skills

A DRAMATIC ENDING

1. What was the steward's day job?

2. What flavour of ice cream would have been offered at the interval?

3. What role was the victim playing?

4. For how long had the list of suggested plays been released before the murderer committed their crime?

5. What role had the murderer been hoping to win?

Detective Skills

COLD COMFORT

1. What were my slippers made of?

2. What was the victim's name?

3. What types of weather had occurred on the day of the murder?

4. How many sets of footprints were shown in the image?

5. What was the outside temperature at midday on the day of the murder?

Detective Skills

THE DIAMOND AND THE ROUGH

1. What had I been planning to eat for breakfast the day after the break in?

2. What was the name of the jewel and watch shop's owner?

3. At what time, in real time, was the smashed watch brought into the shop?

4. What was the name of the square-cut diamond's owner, who was going steady with the would-be recipient?

5. What did Mr Hickory give to me as a gift of gratitude?

Detective Skills

THE PLOT THICKENS

1. What pudding did I mention I make a superb version of?

2. What had Martin's profession been before his retirement?

3. What vegetable had caused a gardener to give up his allotment?

4. In what season of the year was Martin killed?

5. What had Martin been planting on the day he was killed?

6. Which vegetable crop of Martin's had been hidden in the compost?

7. How many pairs of gloves were submitted to the police, including the incomplete pair belonging to the murderer?

8. What had Martin been doing at the allotment just before he was killed?

9. Where was the murderer when Hancock and I confronted them?

10. Which herb was I planning to take home for supper?

SOLUTIONS

Solutions

TICKET TO DIE

12–13: Death by a Thousand Stamps

Each postcard provides a current and following location for the killer. You will also need to know in which country each of the sites that are referred to is located. Combining all of this information together reveals the following travel sequence, from least-recently to most-recently visited country:

- Peru (Machu Picchu)
- Egypt (Nile)
- China (Great Wall)
- France (Eiffel Tower)
- Canada (Niagara Falls)
- South Africa (Table Mountain)
- Japan (Mount Fuji)
- Germany (Berlin)

Therefore the murderer was coming from Germany.

14–15: Some Strings Attached

The letters in each item on every bag label must be rearranged to identify the items in that bag. Reading down the columns on each label:

- Bag 1: Socks, watch, anorak, journal, newspaper, knife
- Bag 2: Bow tie, overcoat, cardigan, mirror, towel, poison
- Bag 3: Dress, vest, magazine, shoes, bullet, wallet
- Bag 4: Trousers, shirt, scarf, gloves, suit, razor

Solutions

Bag 4 only has clothing inside, other than one item: the razor. This bag therefore has the most clothing, so the razor must have been the murder weapon.

16–17: Rather Negative, Actually

The combined images show that Mr Norris was standing on platform 3a:

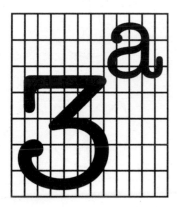

18–19: Death and the Departed

The murderer boarded the 16.48 to Little Bizenforth from platform 6.

The complete list of departures is as follows:

Platform	Time	Destination
2	17.01	Lopton Head
3a	16.32	Drumberry
4	16.30	Stickleton
6	16.48	Little Bizenforth
7b	17.10	St Church

Solutions

20–21: Covering One's Tracks

Having set off from platform 6, the killer was now heading towards the destination labelled A:

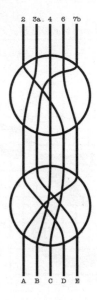

22–23: At Cross Purposes

There are five opportunities to intercept the train:

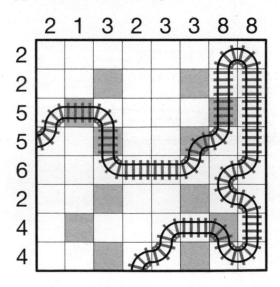

Solutions

24–25: The Final Disguise

The differences can be found as follows:

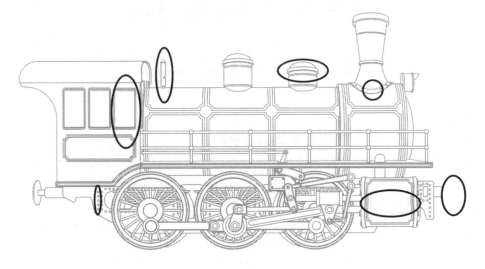

26–27: Time to Name Names

The only complete ticket belongs to a Mr Neville Franklin:

1	TRAIN TICKET
	Mr Neville Franklin

He was, therefore, the murderer.

31: Case Closed

1. Mr Richard Trackson
2. Somewhere near Lake Geneva
3. Mr Weston, the baker
4. Table Mountain

Solutions

A BUMP IN THE ROAD

36–37: A Daring Escape

The stolen car travelled along the following route, beginning at the starred police station and ending at location B:

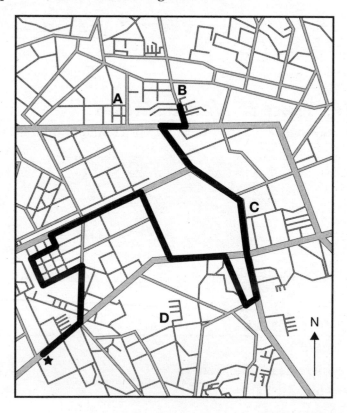

Solutions

38–39: Identifying the Problem

The original number plate looked like this, with the missing sections outlined in the boxes:

So the number plate was EQ84 ODU.

40–41: Something Is Not Quite Adding Up

The value for each of the individual items is as follows:

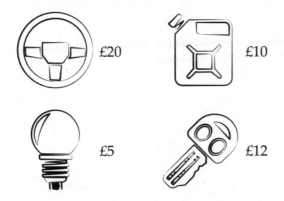

£20

£10

£5

£12

Therefore the total for Alice to pay is £47.

Solutions

42–43: Printing Problems

There is only one complete fingerprint:

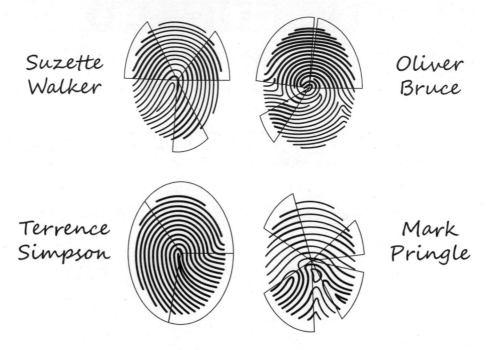

Suzette Walker

Oliver Bruce

Terrence Simpson

Mark Pringle

It belonged to Terrence Simpson – the owner of the garage!

45: Case Closed

1. Snipping – the same as his son, who was on the case of the stolen car
2. Bottle green
3. Her father
4. Seven

Solutions

THE FORCED HAND

50–51: *The Glass Is Quite Empty*

The shards of glass can be rearranged as follows:

Glass C, with the ridged edge, is therefore missing its bottom section.

52–53: *To the Bitter End*

The group were drinking as follows:

Drinker	Glass feature	Drink
Harold	Stem (B)	Water
Grace	Ridge (C)	Ginger beer
Mortimer	Straight side (A)	Cider
Angela	Curved side (D)	Bitter

Grace was drinking out of the ridged glass with the shard missing, C, and is therefore the attacker.

Solutions

54–55: The Drama Unfolds

The napkin can be mentally unfolded as follows:

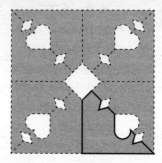

There are four hearts created by the curved shape, and nine diamonds are revealed. The two cards indicated are therefore the four of hearts and the nine of diamonds.

56–57: A Pack of Lies

There are two of the same card – namely, the four of clubs:

These cannot have come from the same, single deck of cards – so either someone is badly organized, or trying to cheat!

59: Case Closed

1. Four
2. Ginger beer, water, cider and bitter.
3. Paul
4. Ten

Solutions

A WHOLE NEW BALL GAME

64–65: A Sequence of Suspicious Events

The results for each month all follow the same pattern. The first score is arbitrary, and then doubled for the second result. From then on, 3 is subtracted, 4 added, 5 subtracted, 6 added, and so on. The results for June should therefore be:

5 – 10 – 7 – 11 – 6 – **12** – **5** – **13**

66–67: Tough to Pin Down

The next player scheduled to purposefully throw their match is Ian. When the pins attached to each name tag are joined with lines according to the team sheets on the facing page, the following image emerges, with the names in each team forming a letter:

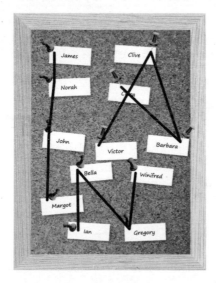

Solutions

68–69: The Loser's Perspective

Only photo A shows the balls in the same configuration as on the magazine page:

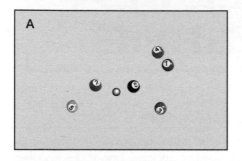
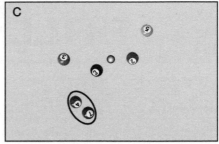
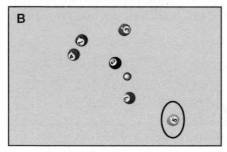
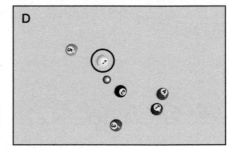

70–71: Time to Grass Them Up

For Gregory to lose all four of his matches, he must have started to play in the second match – since if he had started in the first match and lost them all, he would have played in five of the nine matches.

Bella won the first four matches, and Victor beat Gregory in the sixth, so those results can be marked in. For Victor to play in the sixth game, he must have beaten Bella in the fifth match.

For Bella to beat Gregory three times she must have won match 8 against him, meaning she also won match 7 against Victor. We know Victor won three times, so he must have won the last match, beating Bella.

Mapping out all nine matches with the above deductions gives the following set of results, with each player represented by their initial:

Solutions

Game	1	2	3	4	5	6	7	8	9
Won	B	B	B	B	V	V	B	B	V
Lost	V	G	V	G	B	G	V	G	B

Bella, therefore, was the loser of the final match, and the group's nefarious ringleader.

73 Case Closed

1. Ruffles
2. June
3. Twelve
4. Mint choc chip

Solutions

PAINTED INTO A CORNER

78–79: All in the Family

The remaining suspects are Zelda, John, Simon and Olga.

Three of Oscar's grandparents are ruled out: Martin, Lila and Frank. His cousin Clare and aunt Jane are in Australia, as is Jane's niece Marie. His nephews Joseph and Marcus are ruled out due to their age. Oscar's sister-in-law Anna is ruled out along with her children Flora and Nell, and his mother Molly is above suspicion along with his brother-in-law Henry. Eddie is Zelda's son in law, and Alfred is Lila's son-in-law, so both are also ruled out. That leaves the four prime suspects: Oscar's grandmother Zelda, uncle John, brother Simon and niece Olga.

80–81: A Labyrinth of Lies

The route from one end to the other of the ground floor is as follows:

Ground Floor:

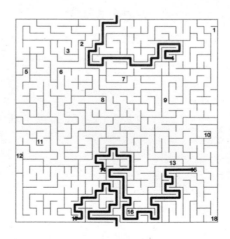

204

Solutions

First Floor:

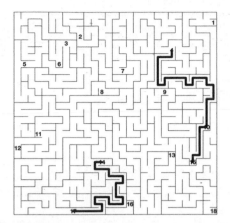

The thief therefore used four staircases: 4, 15, 14 and 17. This rules out any family members older than Oscar, which is therefore Zelda and John, who must both be older then Oscar, since we know John is older than Oscar's mother Molly. The two remaining suspects are therefore Simon and Olga.

82–83: A Note of Panic

The initial letters of each sentence spell out OLGA. The sender has given several clues to examine the sentence openers: 'go back to the very beginning', 'at the start' and 'initial confusion'. The letter, incidentally, was sent by Oscar's sister Marie, who is Olga's mother.

84–85: Pull the Other One

The book to pull is the one marked '12', on the second shelf down.

Solutions

86–87: A Hidden Masterpiece

The painting labelled 'C' is the real masterpiece:

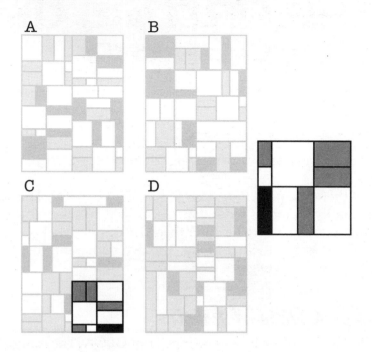

89 Case Closed

1. Vol-au-vents
2. Lila
3. Five
4. Three – as one was the genuine masterpiece

Solutions

THE WRITING ON THE WALL

94–95: A Handy First Clue

The revealed image shows a hand with an arrow pointing to a fingertip.

Marjorie Winkleman was suggesting that fingerprints were a critical piece of evidence when investigating a crime.

96–97: A Sticky End

Each of the stickers indicates which word from that book's title should be read to reveal the message, working from the book at the top of the stack downwards. The book at the top has a '4' sticker, so the fourth word, 'There', should be used. The second book has a '2' sticker, indicating the second word, 'Is', and so on. When all of the words in the stack are extracted in the same way, the following message is revealed: There Is Only One Way To Escape The Library.

Solutions

98–99: In The Bad Books

The flags indicating section 400-499 have been severed:

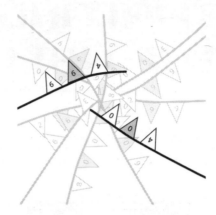

The killer must therefore have been standing in the section of the library indicated by these flags, which according to the guide is reserved for 'Language'.

100–101: Ways and Means

The killer escaped through exit D, at the bottom of the floor plan:

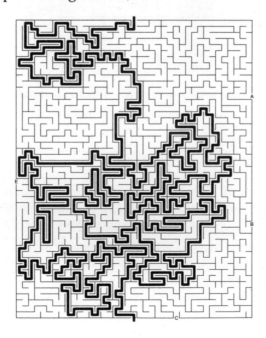

Solutions

102–103: Four Ways to Spot a Killer

The appearances of the four people are as follows:

Hair	Jumper	Transport	Object
Bald	Blue	Running	Newspaper
Brown	Purple	Walking	Scissors
Red	Green	Cycling	Baguette
Blonde	Brown	Motorbike	Handbag

The killer was therefore walking and wearing a purple jumper, and had brown hair.

104–105: The Seal of Disapproval

Most of the stamps are exactly 7 days apart, except for one:

- 01-03 Mrs A Walker
- 08-03 S Wren
- 12-03 P M Gill
- 15-03 Miss T Peck
- 22-03 Dr Smith
- 29-03 Caroline G
- 05-04 Mr M Grant
- 12-04 Kate Waters

P M Gill supposedly took out the book 4 days after S Wren, and 3 days before Miss T Peck. A quick interview with Sofia Wren confirmed that, like her fellow residents, she in fact kept the book for exactly seven days – and Gill's stamp is therefore confirmed as a forgery.

Solutions

106–107: A Signature Move

Two of the signatures are identical:

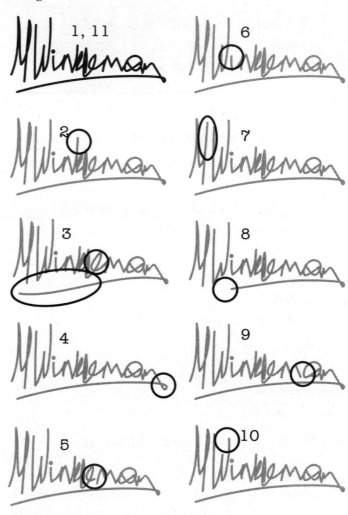

111 Case Closed

1. The Hog and Badger (a local pub)
2. Nine
3. Mrs A Walker
4. 800-899

Solutions

A DRAMATIC ENDING

116–117: A Tragedy of Errors

The complete list of actors, and the roles they played, is as follows:

Role	Actor
Hercules	Roger
Madonna	Sally
Neris	Meera
Oriole	Lindsey
Sven	William
Gloria	Helena
Agnes	Glenda
Vladimir	Max

Sally, who played Madonna, was the victim.

118–119: A Closer Look at Chaos

Suspect 1 is Meera, Suspect 2 is Glenda and Suspect 3 is William:

Meera

Glenda

William

Solutions

120–121: A Tough Act to Follow

Suspect 2 – who has already been established as Glenda – is the one who always lies, and so is the murderer.

Suspect 1 – who we know is Meera – tells us that she always lies; but if this is true, then she must not be lying. She also cannot be the person who always tells the truth, as her statement would not be truthful. By elimination, she must be the person who sometimes lies.

This revelation leaves two possibilities for the second interviewee: Suspect 2, Glenda, lies all the time or none of the time. She claims to tell the truth sometimes, but we know this role has been filled, so she is lying. She must therefore be the one who always lies, and therefore the murderer.

122–123: The Great Pretender

The five plays are as follows:

- CYMBELINE
- HAMLET
- MACBETH
- OTHELLO
- PERICLES

The next play, therefore, was due to be Macbeth.

125 Case Closed

1. George Hillock
2. Roger
3. Tea rooms
4. William Shakespeare

Solutions

130–131: Straight Out of the Blocks

The were 7 opportunities to intercept the victim. There were 56 ice blocks at the beginning of the day, and 49 in the photograph, so 7 must have been taken throughout the course of the day.

132–133: Something's Afoot

The prime suspects are Clive Young and Glen Walker. One of Clive Young's shoes is clearly much bigger than the other, and Glen Walker's footprints show two right footprints:

Glen Walker should be considered Suspect A, and Clive Young should be considered Suspect B.

134–135: When Hell Freezes Over

Suspect B was unaccounted for while the temperature was between -2°C and 0°C, between 6pm and 7pm.

The temperature chart shows the following readings:

Midday	5°C	
1pm	dropped by 2	3°C
2pm	rose by 3	6°C
3pm	dropped by 4	2°C

Solutions

4pm	dropped by 3	-1°C
5pm	rose by 2	1°C
6pm	dropped by 3	-2°C
7pm	rose by 2	0°C
8pm	rose by 5	5°C

Suspect A, Glen Walker, committed the crime.

136–137: The Pyramid Scheme

Davina stood to lose the following amounts at each stage:

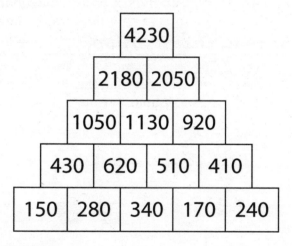

Adding up each of the payments shows that she stood to lose £14,710.

139 Case Closed

1. Peppermint tea
2. 64, in a 4×4×4 arrangement
3. Suzy Feathers
4. 15

Solutions

THE DIAMOND AND THE ROUGH

144–145: A Really Smashing Time

The attack took place at 3pm exactly. For each actual hour passing between the watch being brought in and the watch being smashed, only 54 minutes pass on the watch (as it's running 6 minutes slow every hour). Working forwards from the time shown on the watch when it was brought in (9.02), the following equivalents emerge:

Actual Time	Time on Watch
10am	9.02
11am	9.56
12pm	10.50
1pm	11.44
2pm	12.38
3pm	1.32

146–147: Keep The Cogs Turning

Turning cog 1 anticlockwise turns the rest like this:

Solutions

To open the gate again, cog 2 would have to be turned in the opposite direction to that shown, so the thief would have to turn it clockwise.

148–149: Looking Back and Forth

The recipient's name is Annabelle. The second facet and the fourth/central facet have been reflected, so some parts of the name appear backwards and on the opposite side to their original position:

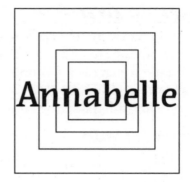

150-151 A Thief of Love

Henry Fuller is the secret admirer – and the would-be thief.

153 Case Closed

1. Oboes and clarinets
2. Richard Wales
3. The Tivertons
4. Six

Solutions

158–159: Allotted Areas

There are 47 distinct rectangular areas – so only Martin was correct.

160–161: Leeked Information

In the order of planting, the gardeners were in their allotments with the following vegetables:

	Person	Plant
1.	Geraldine	Leeks
2.	Petros	Garlic
3.	Suzanna	Cabbage
4.	Martin	Kale
5.	Hans	Turnips
6.	Micah	Chard

Suzanna and Hans are therefore the two people to speak to.

162–163: What's Your Poison?

Reading the plant markers from top to bottom, left page then right page, the following plants with toxic leaves or flowers are labelled:

- DEADLY NIGHTSHADE
- YEW
- AZALEA
- HEMLOCK
- RHUBARB

Solutions

- FOXGLOVE
- MISTLETOE
- OLEANDER
- LILY OF THE VALLEY
- RHODODENDRON

When sorted into alphabetical order, the fifth in the list is LILY OF THE VALLEY – the plant used to poison Martin.

164–165: Breaking New Ground

The borders can be reconstructed as follows:

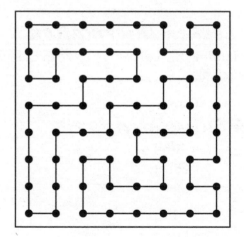

Clearly whoever poisoned Martin had visited nearly every part of his allotment.

Solutions

166–167: May Contain Traces of Murder

The picture that emerged is of a garden fork:

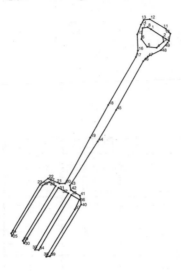

168–169: A Calculated Error

The measurements of the garden plot are as follows:

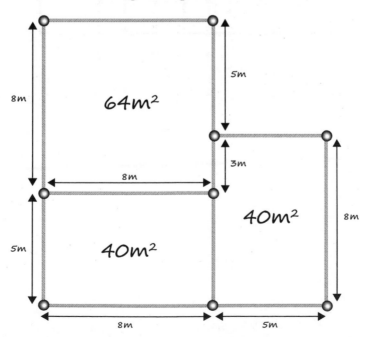

Solutions

The overall area would be 144m², so the cost of the compost to cover it, at £1/m², would be £144.

170–171: Digging the Dirt

There were nine of Martin's prize pumpkins buried in the compost:

1	3	🎃	3	1
🎃		🎃	🎃	3
🎃		3	🎃	🎃
	2		3	🎃
1	🎃	1	1	1

Solutions

172–173: The Gloves Are Off

The gloves can be matched up as follows:

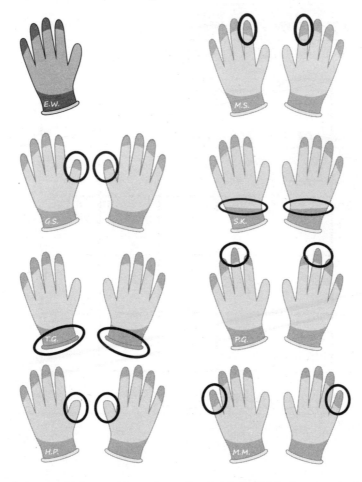

The gardener missing a glove has the initials E.W. So they belong to... Emma Waterman, the allotment supervisor.

177: Case Closed

1. Geraldine
2. Ten
3. Mr Green
4. The Bishop's End Allotment Network, or BEAN

Solutions

DETECTIVE SKILLS

180 Ticket to Die

1. Flintchester
2. A cheese grater
3. Graham – although that might have been his first or last name
4. Mr Norris
5. Seven
6. Bag 2
7. 17.01
8. Geography teacher
9. Travel agent
10. Supper with the vicar

181 A Bump in the Road

1. Claret
2. £12
3. Alice Wallace
4. Journalist
5. Buttercream

182 The Forced Hand

1. The Brass Buckles
2. On a Thursday
3. By the fire, with a crossword puzzle
4. Hanna
5. Three

Solutions

183 A Whole New Ball Game

1. Three: cricket, croquet and bowls
2. Eight
3. 21
4. The Bishop's End Association Magazine, or BEAM
5. Poppily St Martin's

184 Painted into a Corner

1. Butternut Hall
2. With a key
3. Australia
4. 18
5. His sister Marie

185 The Writing on the Wall

1. An overdue library book
2. Mrs Sanderson
3. On the front row
4. Turn back to page 97 for the full list
5. 10
6. 5, labelled A to E
7. A baguette
8. Seven days exactly
9. Signed, Sealed, Deceased
10. All the way to Flintchester!

186 A Dramatic Ending

1. Sheep herding
2. Vanilla
3. Madonna
4. Not long at all – they were released that day
5. Lady Macbeth – the wife of the protagonist, Macbeth

Solutions

187 Cold Comfort

1. Sheepskin
2. Davina Cricket
3. Bad – there was sleet, rain and snow
4. Five
5. 5 degrees Celcius

188 The Diamond and the Rough

1. Kippers
2. Mr Hickory
3. 10am
4. Timothy Winters
5. A delightfully embellished magnifying glass

189 The Plot Thickens

1. A crumble
2. Cobbler
3. Carrots
4. Autumn
5. Kale
6. Pumpkins
7. Eight – seven complete pairs and the murderer's incomplete pair
8. Checking for slugs
9. In a shed
10. Thyme